THE INCREDIBLE DIARY OF...

Timeless Tales

Edited By Donna Samworth

First published in Great Britain in 2023 by:

Young Writers
Remus House
Coltsfoot Drive
Peterborough
PE2 9BF
Telephone: 01733 890066
Website: www.youngwriters.co.uk

Printed and bound in the UK by BookPrintingUK
Website: www.bookprintinguk.com
YB0564E

Foreword

Dear Diary,

You will never guess what I did today! Shall I tell you? Some primary school pupils wrote some diary entries and I got to read them, and they were **EXCELLENT!**

Here at Young Writers we created some bright and funky worksheets along with fun and fabulous (and free) resources to help spark ideas and get inspiration flowing. And it clearly worked because **WOW!!** I can't believe the adventures I've been reading about. Real people, make-believe people, dogs and unicorns, even objects like pencils all feature and these diaries all have one thing in common – they are **JAM-PACKED** with imagination!

Here at Young Writers we want to pass our love of the written word onto the next generation and what better way to do that than to celebrate their writing by publishing it in a book! It sets their work free from homework books and notepads and puts it where it deserves to be – **OUT IN THE WORLD!**

Each awesome author in this book should be **SUPER PROUD** of themselves, and now they've got proof of their imagination, their ideas and their creativity in black and white, to look back on in years to come!

Contents

Faith L Wilson (10)	78
Yahya Khan (9)	80
Parisa Halliru (9)	82
Lily-Rae Jubbs (8)	84
Aleena Halliru (8)	86
Aaron Farrell (8)	87

Great Easton Primary School, Great Easton

Oscar Salt (8)	88
Eva Bailey (9)	89
Ethan Boevé (8)	90
Camryn Mcintyre (8)	91
Freddie (8)	92
Tobias Allen Williams (8)	93
Riley Parker (8)	94
George Luckin (8)	95
Kyle Morris (8)	96

St John's CE Primary School, Keele

Jessica Ryder (8)	97
Ashleigh McKinson (8)	98
William Bryan (8)	99
Emily Bucknall (8)	100
Elliot Deaville (8)	101
Charlie Boulton (9)	102
Evelyn Rose Kamarauskas (8)	103
Callum Mckinon (8)	104
Erdem Misirli (7)	105
Harrison Currie (7)	106
Nawfal Shivji (8)	107
Solomon Karimi (8)	108

St Mary's CE Primary School, Greenfield

Florence Penney (9)	109
Scarlett Gunton (9)	110
Hayden Moss (9)	112
Theodore Gifford-Dixon (9)	113
Lucy Hill (9)	114

Bill Southall (9)	115
Jessica Whiteley (9)	116
Nina Buckley (9)	117
Lochlan Holland (9)	118
Summer Bowker (9)	119
Nile Holland (9)	120
Laura Ratcliff (9)	121
Harry Bennett (9)	122
Freddie Taylor (9)	123
Geoffrey Podmore (9)	124
Darcey Fitzpatrick (9)	125
Freya Doxford (9)	126
Enzo Bailey (9)	127

St Nicholas CE Primary School, Reading

Lola Massarella (10)	128
William Randles (10)	130
Adam Woodward (10)	132
Dhiya Singaravelan (10)	134
Gianne Hui (10)	135
Martha May Piggins (10)	136
Lily Rand (10)	137
Zoe Henderson (10)	138
Amelia Loader (10)	139
Noah Westerling (10)	140
Oscar Dewey (10)	141
Violet Boyden (10)	142
Lucas Jaworski (9)	143
Sammy Jones (9)	144
Willow Gregory (10)	145
Caleb Chan (10)	146
Giovanna Wan (10)	147

St Patrick's Catholic Primary School, Birmingham

Monjolaoluwa Olusola (10)	148
Viktoria Wojcik (10)	150
Hannah Vipin (10)	152
Stacey Bansah (10)	153
Georgina Sarker (10)	154
Avneet Kaur (9)	155

The Diaries

A Day In The Life Of My Dog

Dear Diary,

As I woke up I found out that my so annoying owner woke up before me so I couldn't jump on her. Then I tried to eat my owner's food but she told me to stop and sit. Sadly I walked away, only I wanted some food. Eventually she decided to pour me some food into a bowl and then walked off. Why does she need to go all the time? I followed her to the bathroom. She put a weird thing in her mouth, do you know what it is?

Anyway, she had a salad for lunch and I knew straight away that I couldn't have it but I sat down anyway. I played and then after a long wait I was fed again.

At night I went to the toilet in the house and then she made me go to bed and sleep. Later she went to bed and when I woke up it was the morning.

Tilly Dixon (10)

Cadbury Heath Primary School, Warmley

A Day In The Life Of Allia Richards

Dear Diary,

You wouldn't believe the series of events that happened last night. I was fast asleep and dreaming about reflecting on the past day when a thunderous roar woke me with a start. Feeling for the light switch, I fumbled around in the darkness. After what felt like forever, I found it and clicked it on. Everything looked normal except, wait, there was something on the floor. I bent down to pick it up and held it up to the light. It had illuminated scratchy handwriting. It was a message. I understood what the symbols meant. The message read: 'Come, there is trouble on the Bleak Isle'. The Bleak Isle was a dangerous, jagged rock far out at sea and it was so dangerous that nobody dared to go there.

Quickly I pulled my jacket over my night dress and grabbed my parachute and tiptoed downstairs. Father was snoring and I heard him roll over in bed. As soon as I was outside I strapped up my parachute. It was a long journey to Bleak Isle but it would be worth it to save this world.

I jumped on the clifftop, feeling the fresh deep night air brush my cheeks. Suddenly I could see something flashing on the horizon. Evil was at work. Directing my parachute in that direction, I headed towards Bleak Isle. It seemed like hours of flying but the parachute finally touched down on the rock itself. The light flashing from it was blinding.

I closed my eyes for a minute before opening them and all of a sudden I knew what I had to do. Leaping across the gap like a bird in flight, I pounced onto the rock and smashed the globe into pieces. I had won.

Clara Exton (10)

Cadbury Heath Primary School, Warmley

The Attachment Of The Kaiju

Dear Diary,

The most bizarre thing happened today. Me and my friends Katrina and Maokay were all going to a haunted house. As soon as I found this old necklace I put it on and some kind of demon appeared. We all sprinted out knowing that something was now chasing us and it was on all fours chasing us. Then, all of a sudden, when I took off the necklace it got stuck and wouldn't leave me.

When I got back home from this almost terrifying ordeal I tried to see what the demon was feeling and locked on its eyes.

"What are you looking at?" Its voice was filled with malice. Its face was filled with a lust for violence. I screamed at its sudden words and fell off my bed.

"When will you leave me alone?" I asked in a concerned but intrigued tone.

The response was, "I am unable to."

Slowly I stepped away as his words came. "Is there any way in which you can leave me alone?" I asked again.

"Look it up," he grumbled so I grabbed the laptop that was on my bed. I nodded at the demon and slowly opened the search engine on how to get rid of a demon. The first step was to find a temple located in the country Russia and a helper would guide me but I had to bear in mind this was very risky and dangerous but for the second point I was warned it would be difficult without the help of the demon...

Alaylah Dean (10)
Cadbury Heath Primary School, Warmley

My Happy Day

Dear Diary,

I had the most amazing day of my life, my mum, dad and all my friends surprised me with this amazing brown and white horse called Rex at a yard close by. He is very well-behaved on the roads and will make a good dressage horse as well as being good at everything else. When they surprised me I felt very happy and excited to start my new journey with the horse. It was going so well and we had been on some hacks in the woods and had lots of schooling. I am now very excited because we are going to our very first show and doing a dressage test. I am a very happy girl and I am looking forward to lots of adventures.

Lily-Mai Mahony (10)

Cadbury Heath Primary School, Warmley

Flo's Flotsam Diary

Dear Diary,

Today has been good. First I woke up and had some cereal. It was so yummy. Then I got to open my presents because it was my birthday. For my birthday treat I went to the beach. At the beach I read a book, then I did some gymnastics. I did splits and backbends. Then I did a cartwheel and I landed on something hard. It was a camera.

Soon it was time for lunch and I had a sandwich. I showed Dad the camera and he said it was very old. He opened it for me. I saw lots of strange things. The first picture was so cool, it was turtles rapping. The second was dolphins snorkelling. I was so surprised. The last picture was crabs playing rounders. I felt so lucky to be able to see these pictures. Then I went to see my mum and dad and my mum said I should maybe put the camera back into the sea so someone else could find it. It was a good idea so I did that.

After that, I made sandcastles and swam in the sea. Then I got an ice cream. After that we went home and had delicious pizza. Now I am about to close my eyes and dream about who will find the camera next.

Florence Colley (8)

Castel Primary School, Castel

A Flotsam Diary

Dear Diary,

Yesterday was one of the best days of my life. Firstly I had my breakfast and I had a bacon and sausage sandwich with a glass of orange juice and it was so yummy. Next I went to the gym because I needed to practise for a fight at the weekend and I'm against Joel Stephalem. He sucks but I'm probably going to win. There was no time to lose otherwise my parents would kill me!

After that I went to the beach but there was a thunderstorm. I let out a sigh of relief because by the time we were at the beach the storm had cleared. Wow, I can't believe I survived that! At least it was over and I could set out all of my gear. I started to play football but all of a sudden I kicked something as hard as solid rock. "Ouch!" I yelled.

Charlie, my friend, said, "You should wear shoes more often, Benjamin!"

"No!" I shouted.

When I recovered from my injury I dug out the 'thing' and I found out that it was an old-fashioned camera! I pressed a button and it opened and inside I found some film so I took it to a one-hour photo shop. Exhausted I went in and threw the film on the desk. "Hurry up, please!" I said.

After a whole hour I looked at the printed photos and I jumped in shock when I saw what was on them: SpongeBob! Electric Underwater City! Raining tacos underwater! Huh? I knew I needed to hide the photos so I put them under my car seat and went home. I played tennis outside and then by the light of the moon I was fast asleep.

Bodhi Gallienne (7)
Castel Primary School, Castel

Luke's Flotsam Diary

Dear Diary,

Today was a pretty weird day. I was eating my breakfast and I found a note and it said 'Meet me in the living room'. I didn't know if I should but I went and my mum just wanted to tell me we were going to the beach. I started to pack my beach bag. "Mum, I'm just packing my beach bag," I said. "Okay," she said.

We went to the beach and I was playing in the sand and very close to the water and I built a sandcastle. Then a wave came and broke it. Then a bigger one came and it took me in, it was fun but scary at the same time. Then I felt something on my arm. It was a camera.

Once I got back to the sand I ran to my parents and shouted, "Mum, Dad, look what I have found. It's a camera! Can we go to the photoshop and see if they can help?"

"Of course," they said.

We went to the photoshop and I saw the photos. There were snorkelling dolphins, octopuses wearing tin can hats and fish with dog paws as fins! I got super scared and then I took a photo of me because I saw some other kids who had taken pictures of themselves. After that I threw the camera back into the ocean and I will always remember this day!

Skyla-Mai Garnham (8)

Castel Primary School, Castel

A Flotsam Diary

Dear Diary,

It was my birthday, I had the best time ever! I opened all my presents before school and one was a football and it was really cool. I wasn't allowed to take my other football to school in case I lost it and now I had another that I could take to school. After school, I went to the park for an hour and then I went to the park cafe and played on my iPad. Then I went to the swimming pool for an hour and then I went to bed.

I woke up and I played football and then I went to school. It was home time and I went to the beach and dug deep in the sand. I put my toy in the sea and then I went in the sea. I played football after and kicked my ball so hard that it made a hole and I saw a camera. I picked it up and took it to the police. They were happy I gave it to them.

I went home and went in the pool until it was time for my tea. I then went to sleep for a bit and when I woke up I gave my dad a hug for how nice he was to give me money to buy something. Then I went back to sleep. I love my sleep. After that my dad made pizza and it was delicious. I then went back to the beach and made a sandcastle and stayed for an hour. It was really fun. I had food as well.

Ollie Cooney (8)

Castel Primary School, Castel

A Flotsam Diary

Dear Diary,

Today was a weird day. The day started like any other day when I got out of bed and went for breakfast. For breakfast I had Cheerios then I got in the car and went for a journey to the beach. When I got to the beach I made a sandcastle and then after the sandcastle, my mum said, "Come and get your swimmers on to go swimming."
I said, "Okay Mum, I'm coming."
When I was swimming I saw a big wave and it hit me and took me under. Underwater I saw a camera. When I saw the camera I swam and picked it up and took it to my mum. She told me to open it so I did. It was a digital camera. I saw something very weird and a bit creepy. I showed it to Mum and she was petrified. In the first picture there was a giant stinging jellyfish which was so creepy my mum nearly fainted. The next one was a giant seahorse which was cool but it was fighting which was not nice. The final picture was Sea Star Island and all the people there were screaming like babies. I took a picture of me and threw the camera back into the sea.

We went home and for dinner had an Italian pizza and then I went to bed and started writing in this diary.

Isaac Ashman (8)

Castel Primary School, Castel

A Flotsam Diary

Dear Diary,

I was doing gymnastics in my lounge for half an hour and then my mum said we were going to the beach. I was jumping around and I was super excited. After that we got into the car and headed to the beach. Woo!

When we got there I built a huge sandcastle and it was so fun. Then we saw my cousins and we headed over to them to have lunch and we had some yummy pizza. I love pizza. Then I went snorkelling and I saw a camera and it looked cool. I have never seen anything like it.

I took it up to the top of the beach to show my family and they were amazed. They had gone crabbing and they caught three baby crabs and two massive crabs. I was so shocked. Our family opened the camera and there were so many photographs. I kept them safe. We wondered what colour it was, it was black and was so dark and creepy.

I let it go back into the sea so I threw it off a rock. The rock was so big and I did not want to let it go. Finally I went home and then I had a bath and washed my hair. I had sausages and mash for dinner and then I watched TV for half an hour. I then started writing this diary.

Evie Ogier (7)
Castel Primary School, Castel

Eddy's Flotsam Diary

Dear Diary,

Today has been an unusual day. Firstly I had a little snack while playing on my Switch and my mum said, "Get ready for the beach, we are going soon!" As I got ready I watched a story on YouTube.

I got in the car and got my bodyboard ready and when we got to the beach I started to make a massive sandcastle and when I had finished I was amazed with myself. "Wow!" I said to myself.

After my brother wanted to go in the sea and we saw some big waves that were as big as elephants. After that my mum came down to check on us. After that a massive wave came and knocked me off my bodyboard and then I saw a camera. I could not believe my eyes. When I saw the pictures I was shocked. I saw a seahorse snorkelling and a jellyfish that looked like Squidward.

I got dried and then I showed my mum and dad as the lifeguard did not want to know. We then took it to Fitzgerald's and he said it was an underwater camera and I wondered who took the pictures.

We explored the camera further then went back home and when we went back to the beach we saw another big wave...

Eddy Naftel (8)

Castel Primary School, Castel

James' Flotsam Diary

Dear Diary,

Today was a very unusual day. First I woke up and had breakfast which was marmalade on toast. Once I had finished I got dressed and brushed my teeth. My mum said, "Get ready for breakfast because we are leaving soon."

I went back to my room and I got my swimmers and grabbed my snorkel and bucket and spade. then I headed to the beach.

When we got to the beach I pulled out my snorkelling gear and walked to the pier. I jumped off the pier. After a while of snorkelling, I found a rusty, old fork, a spear gun with no spear probably from years ago and also an old camera which seemed very old.

I swam back to the pier to look at the pictures if it had any, which it did! What I saw was shocking! There was a jellyfish doing the tango with a shark, an octopus playing the trumpet and a crowd of fish as an underwater supermarket with shells as trolleys! I was so shocked. I didn't know what to do with the photos and after thinking for an hour I decided to keep it a secret.

Once I got home I brushed my teeth and got undressed and I did some reading and went to bed.

Charlie Curtis (8)

Castel Primary School, Castel

A Flotsam Diary

Dear Diary,

In the morning at 9:34am I just had my breakfast and it was yummy. I had toast and my sister had Cheerios. After that we were riding bikes and it was my sister's birthday. We had to do what she wanted to do. Next we went to the beach and I ran so fast so I could get the unicorn bucket. We had a sandcastle competition and I won, yay!

We went and jumped into the ocean. When I was swimming, something hit my foot. I swam back to shore to see what it was. A book? Cake? No, it was a camera! I looked inside and it still had some film so I took it to a photoshop and I had to wait for one hour.

I looked at the first photo of a fish but it wasn't a normal kind of fish, it was a robot fish. Anyways, I looked at the second one and there was a sofa with an octopus reading a book with some fish. I looked at the third picture and saw a pufferfish in a hot-air balloon with fish in the basket. OMG!

I rushed back to the beach and I realised I should take a picture of myself as well. Sadly the day was over and I threw the camera back onto the ocean.

Sophia Strawbridge (8)

Castel Primary School, Castel

A Flotsam Diary

Dear Diary,

Today I woke up knowing it was going to be a great day. I jumped out of bed, went downstairs and ate my breakfast. After that I got dressed and brushed my teeth. A couple of hours later I went to the beach and I went swimming in the sea. Suddenly, out of the corner of my eye, I saw something. I swam closer and closer and suddenly I saw a camera and it was an underwater one. I immediately opened the camera and took the film to a lady to print the photos. It took two hours. Finally I got to see the photos and I couldn't believe what I could see. The first picture was of tons of robot jellyfish. The second was a stingray watching TV. The third was of mermaids on rocks. Lots of other people were in the photos so I grabbed my magnifying glass to take a closer look. At last I located the first person to have found the camera.

Soon it was time to go home. I didn't have any dinner because I was so tired. I brushed my teeth again and went to bed and started writing this.

Alfie Irlen (8)

Castel Primary School, Castel

Jasmine's Flotsam Diary

Dear Diary,

Today was an interesting day. First I woke up and ate my breakfast. Today I had waffles and they were really yummy. I got into my dad's car and we drove to the beach. When we got there the first thing we did was build sandcastles and after that I went for a swim. A giant piece of seaweed got tangled around my ankle and I swam back to shore to untangle it. In the seaweed I found an underwater camera! I took the film out and ran to the nearest camera shop.

After waiting for one hour, I started looking through the photos. They were incredible. There were lots of people and they looked like they came from Victorian times. I took a photo of myself and I put the camera carefully on top of a bucket and used a spade to press the button so it could take another picture. The second time though a monster wave came and it washed the photos away. I was disappointed but knew what I had to do. I threw the camera back into the sea so someone else could have the same adventure I had.

Meadow Knight (8)
Castel Primary School, Castel

Luke's Flotsam Diary

Dear Diary,

First I got up and then I got dressed. I brushed my teeth and then I ate my breakfast. I celebrated my birthday and I went to the beach. My lunch was so yummy. Then I went for a little swim. I got dry and then I found an underwater camera. I picked it up, looked at it and then threw it back in the ocean. Then I went home, played some games and fell asleep. I dreamt about the weird pictures I had found on the camera I found earlier today, they were so weird.

I woke up and went to the beach. I swam and grabbed the camera again. The pictures were weird. One had not just a fish but a robot one! Then another had a blue fish which was surrounded by furniture and one other had a fish that had a lamp. Next there was a pufferfish in a hot-air balloon with fish inside the basket and water splashing. Next I saw turtles in houses and aliens in flying saucers with some fish and seahorses! There were also pictures of girls and boys holding pictures of girls and boys!

Nathan Rigby (7)
Castel Primary School, Castel

Owyn's Flotsam Diary

Dear Diary,

Today was the weirdest day ever. I got up and I was in a rush because my brother had to go to Squirrels. I quickly ate my breakfast and then we got dressed and after dropping my brother off at Squirrels we went to the beach.

I went for a swim and found it very cold. Then I came back to the beach and found out my brother was back so we went to catch some jellyfish. I went to catch one and got tangled up. Then one stung me and I was screaming so loud my parents came running. Something was next to my leg and it made a mark. I grabbed the box-like thing and I took a look at it. A label read 'underwater camera'. I asked Mum if I could go to Bob's camera shop and she said yes.

I ran up the beach and gave the camera to a lady. I had to wait ages but I got the photos and there were pictures of octopuses reading books and aliens and dolphins snorkelling! I also saw a starfish that looked 2,000 feet tall!

Olwyn Meegan Flatres (8)
Castel Primary School, Castel

Niamh's Flotsam Diary

Dear Diary,

Today was a very busy day! When I woke up I had my favourite breakfast and then we went to the beach which was nice. When we got to the beach I got changed and we went for a swim in the nice cool sea. After that I went rock pooling and I found a crab and then found a mysterious camera on the seashore. I went to grab it and it said 'underwater camera'. I went to ask everyone if it was theirs but no one claimed it so I gave all the photos into the shop and then I took a look the pictures. I saw robot fish, octopuses and sardines, a pufferfish in a hot-air balloon and alien starfish. I also saw people and they were taking photos of themselves. I took a picture of myself and then threw the camera back into the ocean.

The camera could now catch many more sea animals like squid, seahorses, birds and dolphins, not to mention Antarctica and then it will wash up on another shore for another person to find.

Niamh McGrath (8)

Castel Primary School, Castel

A Flotsam Diary

Dear Diary,

I woke up in my bedroom, it was wonderful outside. I went downstairs and had my breakfast and I loved my waffles. I then went to the bathroom and brushed my teeth and I jumped in the car and we were off to the beach. I got my bucket and spade out of my rucksack and I built a sandcastle. Then I felt something in the sand. I got it out and it was a camera. I tried to get the photos out of the camera but I then realised I had to take it to a one-hour photo shop.

When I got the photos back I was shocked to see a robot fish and octopus and some other weird things. I couldn't believe my eyes when I saw them all. It took a whole hour to believe it! I saw a person in one of them and the person was holding a photo of another person and I was so confused. I needed to take a photo of myself so I did and I went home.

At home I got into my PJs and had pasta, tuna, cheese and mayo.

Violet Bishop (8)

Castel Primary School, Castel

A Flotsam Diary

Dear Diary,

When I woke up I was very excited because it was my birthday. It was a bank holiday and my mum said we were going to the beach. I was very excited. Before I could say another word my mum said, "It's for a special treat because it's your birthday!"

We went at 10am and went to the beach and had lots of fun. I went into the sea and I stubbed my toe. I called my mum and she came running and was shocked. "You found it!" she said.

"Found what?"

"I don't know but look."

When we got out of the sea I found a camera. I took the camera to a special shop to get the photos printed. It took an hour.

After the hour, I ran back hoping they were not in the sea and they were not. I looked at the pictures and then I took a picture of myself and threw the camera back into the sea. I said goodbye and then went home.

JoJo De Mouilpied (8)
Castel Primary School, Castel

A Flotsam Diary

Dear Diary,

Today was my birthday, I was shocked. I got out of bed and I went downstairs and I saw tons of presents. I wanted to open them immediately but my mum said to wait. Boring! Then she said I could open one envelope. I did.

I ate my breakfast after that and my dad came and I got to open my presents. Then we went to the beach and when I got to the beach I went straight into the sea. I dived right down to the very bottom and I saw something unusual. I dived down even further and I saw a snorkeling dolphin.

I got out and kicked a camera and it really hurt. I pulled it up and lots of photos fell out of people holding other people. I then told my parents and they didn't really care. I got the last photo and then I took a photo of me holding the last photo. Suddenly a massive wave crashed into me so I threw the camera back into the sea and ran away forever.

Jake McCarthy (8)
Castel Primary School, Castel

Clair's Flotsam Diary

Dear Diary,

Today was an unexpected day. First I got out of bed and then I went to an ice cream shop. When I got there I saw my good friends Mary and Skyla with vanilla ice cream. I invited them to the beach. We hopped in the car to go to the beach.

When we got to the beach I spread out a blanket on the sand and we were just sunbathing on it when I saw something floating in the water. I grabbed it and wiped it and it was a camera. There was a big red button on the side so I pressed it and inside was a big zipped-up bag with pictures inside. We looked at the pictures and saw a crab playing a piano with a hat and there was a ghost which was really odd. We didn't know what to do so we asked our parents for help and then decided to throw it back into the ocean.

I then hopped in the car and when I got back I took a shower, had dinner then got into bed.

Kourtney John (8)

Castel Primary School, Castel

Maia's Flotsam Diary

Dear Diary,

Today was a very unusual day. First I got up out of bed and I got dressed. Then I looked in the mirror and my hair looked like ten bird nests in one. After what felt like an hour of brushing and tidying I finally got my hair back to normal and then I had my breakfast.

My parents surprised me with a beach trip but a crab kept pinching my toes and then I went into the sea and I stepped on something sharp. I thought it was the crab but it wasn't, it was an old, rusty camera. I looked at the pictures and you won't guess what I saw! There were snorkelling dolphins, jellyfish riding blue whales and a sea snake playing the trumpet and the piano at the same time while fish were tap dancing! I asked my mum and dad what to do with the camera and they said they didn't know.

I'm now in bed wondering if I should get rid of it or not...

Mary Ford (8)

Castel Primary School, Castel

A Flotsam Diary

Dear Diary,

Today was a busy day. Firstly my mum told me to go downstairs for breakfast and I told my mum I wanted pancakes with honey on the top. After that my mum told me we were going to the beach. I was so excited so I hopped into my mum's red car and we drove to the beach.

When we got to the beach we ran straight into the water and started swimming and then I ran out of the water and my foot hit something hard. I looked down and it was a camera. I picked it up and opened it up and I saw some photos. Then I took three photos and left the camera and then I threw it back into the ocean and my mum told me we had to go home for dinner. I was so sad and I didn't want to go home. I was hungry though so I packed up and we went home for dinner.

At home I had pizza and then I put the photos under my pillow and went to sleep.

Charlotte Kinsey (8)
Castel Primary School, Castel

A Flotsam Diary

Dear Diary,

Yesterday was a weird day. First I got up and ate breakfast which was peanut butter and jelly sandwiches and cereal. Then I got dressed and we got in the car and drove to the beach.

When we got to the beach I played with my brothers Fionn and Liam. We met up with some friends Theo and Finnley. We went sand duning and I hit my foot on a camera, it must been washed up by the sea. We took it to my parents and we pried it open with a stick, inside we found the camera film. We found a camera film and we took it to the shop and it took ages to develop the photos.

When we got the photos you won't believe what we saw... We saw penguins, blobfish, mermaids and turtles! We then went on my Dad's paddle board and chucked the camera into the sea.

We went home and ate a big, juicy, fat burger with ketchup and chips.

Liam Tansell (8)

Castel Primary School, Castel

A Flotsam Diary

Dear Diary,

When I got up I got out of my bed, brushed my teeth and went downstairs. I had breakfast and I had a croissant, it was delicious. I then got ready for the beach. I got in my car and went to the beach where we brought a kayak. I then played football with my cousin. When I went to kick the ball, I kicked something and uncovered it with my hands. It was an underwater camera. I picked open the hatch with a stick and a rock and I took the film to a one-hour photo shop to get the photos printed.

When they were printed I took the camera back to the beach and it started to rain. My mum and dad then said, "Let's go home!" so we packed up and just before we went I threw the camera back into the sea.

When we got back I had pizza for tea and when I got back into bed I finished writing this diary.

Quinn Baldock (8)

Castel Primary School, Castel

A Flotsam Diary

Dear Diary,

Today I had a very weird day. When I got up I had pancakes with golden syrup. they were tasty. I brushed my teeth for two minutes and then got dressed. When I finished I went to the beach. I jumped on the sand dunes and then I went rock climbing. I found a beach ball when I was climbing. I went for lunch a little later and then I went for a swim. Just when a wave came in I hit my foot on something hard. I picked it up and it was a camera. It looked old so I got out of the sea and looked at it. Then I found some photos and they were inside of the camera. I looked at the photos and I saw a snorkelling dolphin in a bus swimming around and I said, "Wow!"

It was soon time for tea so I had hot dogs with chicken skewers and it was so yummy. Then I brushed my teeth and went to bed.

Theo Leale (8)

Castel Primary School, Castel

Max's Flotsam Diary

Dear Diary,

Today has been an amazing day! I was playing on my Switch when my mum said we were going to the beach. Me and my sister were super excited. I was going snorkelling. We hopped in the car and I saw some really colourful birds.

Then we got to the beach. I was snorkelling in the sea and in the sea I saw a camera. I grabbed it in my hand and then I went snorkelling back to the beach.

I opened the camera and I found some pictures. The first picture had a surfing seal and a fish flying next to it. Next I saw a sandcastle with shiny shells next to it. Next there were some crabs next to a sandcastle with a pool of water for the fish and crabs. I loved it and then took a picture of me on the camera.

Sadly we had to go home so I did. We had pizza for dinner and then I went to bed.

Max Butterfield (8)

Castel Primary School, Castel

Phoebe's Flotsam Diary

Dear Diary,

Today was amazing! I ate breakfast and it was Coco Pops. It was delicious and it was my favourite. Yum! After that I went to the beach in my mum's car. Wow, it looked so much fun. I jumped out of the car with excitement. "Yippee!" I said. I then played in the sea until... a camera washed up. I was shocked. I finally grabbed it and it was wrapped in slippery seaweed. "Yuck!" I said. I took it over and showed my mum and we drove over to the printer's shop. We waited an hour until they were ready. My jaw then dropped open in shock. I saw a pink mermaid in one picture and a scary fish in another picture! There was also a goldfish in another picture. How cool!

After looking at the pictures I went home.

Phoebe Eaton (8)
Castel Primary School, Castel

A Flotsam Diary

Dear Diary,

This morning I woke up and saw it was my birthday. Then my mum came in with breakfast and it was boiled egg - yummy! Next we went to the beach and I went straight into the sea. It was cold. I even went snorkelling.

Suddenly I saw a camera. I picked up the camera and took it to my mum and dad. I opened the camera and looked at the photos. In the camera was a photo of some dolphins. They were so cool! I was so excited! The next picture was of some children holding pictures of more children so I did it as well. It looked so cool. There was a mum seahorse and a dad seahorse. So cute!

I put the camera back in the sea and for tea I had pasta. I was so lucky I went to the beach and now I am writing all about my day.

Isabella Mauger (7)
Castel Primary School, Castel

Elodie's Weird But Wonderful Diary

Dear Diary,

Today was my birthday and I will tell you about it. First I woke up and got to open all my presents and my sister was jealous. Then I made fluffy pancakes and they were yummy.

We then went out and we went on a boat. From the boat we went straight to the beach. I read my Tom Gates and the book was awesome!

I had some lunch and I did some cartwheels. While I was doing cartwheels I hit something. It was a camera. I picked it up and pressed it to open it. I saw lots of different photos. One photo had dolphins snorkelling instead of people!

I then chucked the camera back onto the sea and went home. Me and my family had pizza for tea and finally I went to bed.

Elodie Kenealy (8)
Castel Primary School, Castel

Jackson's Flotsam Diary

Dear Diary,

I woke up this morning and I brushed my teeth, got dressed and then I had my breakfast and went to the beach.

At the beach I went snorkelling and then I went into the sea. I saw some crabs and some turtles and some dolphins, then some octopuses and a mermaid and lots of fish and even some jellyfish... I made a sandcastle and then I went rock pooling and then surfing. I saw a camera in the sea and I picked it up and kept it. I looked inside and I saw lots of photos so I decided to take a photo of myself and then I threw it back into the sea. Finally I went home and before we had dinner we went swimming and now I am in bed.

Mia Le Tissier (8)
Castel Primary School, Castel

A Flotsam Diary

Dear Diary,

Firstly I ate Cornflakes and toast with delicious jam and chocolate spread, yum! Next we drove to the beach and it was fun to drive to the beach because we played I spy.

When we got to the beach I went in the sea and found an interesting camera. When I got the camera I took a picture of myself and after that I took it to a lady and she showed me where to put the pictures. I was so excited when I saw one of the pictures. It was a bit strange because it was an octopus reading a book. I looked at all the pictures then threw the camera back into the sea so someone else could find the camera.

Skyler Du Port (8)

Castel Primary School, Castel

A Flotsam Diary

Dear Diary,

Firstly I got out of bed and then I had a weird breakfast that was Weetabix, cornflakes and Rice Krispies. Next we cycled to the beach. I was so hot. I built a huge sandcastle with my dad and it looked amazing. After that I went swimming and there was a gigantic wave and something hard hit me. It was a strange camera. I pressed the button on the camera and it opened up and I saw some extraordinary pictures from under the ocean. Then I put it back in the sea for someone else to find and went home and had chicken nuggets for tea. Yummy!

Isaac Conner (8)
Castel Primary School, Castel

A Flotsam Diary

Dear Diary,

I ran downstairs and I had my breakfast. I had Nutella on toast and Mum had a surprise, we were going to the beach - yay! Then Mum said we were walking and I was sad. When we got there we went snorkelling and I was stabbed by an alligator. Its teeth made me bleed on my leg. Then I got my RC car and went vroom, vroom, vroom. We were in the car and it broke. I had lunch at McDonald's and then I had pizza - yum. We then walked home.

Alfie Ferbrache (7)
Castel Primary School, Castel

A Flotsam Diary

Dear Diary,

Yesterday I woke up and got dressed and then went downstairs for breakfast. It was Shreddies, yummy! Then we got into my dad's car and we drove to the beach.

At the beach I saw an old-fashioned camera and then I saw the pictures and screamed. There was a shark fighting with its prey! I threw the camera back into the sea.

I loved the beach and at the end of the day I had pizza for tea which is my favourite!

Logan Spicer (8)

Castel Primary School, Castel

A Flotsam Diary

Dear Diary,

I woke up and got dressed and had Coco Pops for breakfast. Then I put my shoes on and I went to the beach. I went rock pooling with my sisters and when my mum called us it was lunchtime. It was delicious. I had ham sandwiches and they were yum.

Later I went swimming and I found a camera. I found a photo of a shark eating fish and I took the camera home and had toasties for tea.

Alfred Robilliard (8)

Castel Primary School, Castel

Kenny And His Love For Grass

Dear Diary,

My name's Kenny and I'm a sheep. Okay, I love grass, it's amazing! One day I woke up on a miserable, rainy day. Ugh! I was starving. I got up to go and eat and walked to my hut to see... mud! Horrible, yucky, sticky mud and no grass. No food! Ugh, I was so hungry so I decided to go somewhere else.

Day one: I walked far but I got so tired that I had to take a nap.

Day two: I woke up and kept walking. I could hardly sleep that night I was so hungry. Because I couldn't sleep I kept walking. When I decided I had walked enough I went to sleep.

Day three: When I woke up there were only mountains but there was a fresh patch of grass (which I couldn't see as it was dark!) around me. Wait, grass! I ran over and took a bite. Yummy! Lucky for me I saw a sleeping hut and there I had found my new home.

Kaitlyn Murray (10)

Craigowl Primary School, Dundee

Diary Of Frodo Baggins

Dear Diary,

It's been a while since I left Mordor and since the eye of Mordor... It started when I had a staring competition with him and kept saying, "Stop it! Stop staring!"

Then he said, "I am watching you!" but we were staring at each other, right, as because I looked at him, he looked at me.

The next night tens of thousands of Orcs ravaged Helm's Deep and me, the dwarves, elves and Gandalf and all the swordsmen fought all night. We beat most of them. The sun drove the rest away. Then we all went on the path to the dead and the undead soldiers tried to get in the way. I just call them Dark Jimmys and the king is Darkest Jimmy. We beat them. The king said he would help us win the war.

It was soon time to win. Me and Sam went to Mount Doom and there was lava everywhere, it was a bad thing. The others and Gandalf continued fighting while we travelled through Mount Doom. Me and Sam then got to a volcano where we destroyed the ring. Before I did it, Golem came and grabbed the ring but he fell in the lava.

Me and Sam nearly fell in the lava but we both climbed out. The eye of Mordor then fell off his pedestal and was destroyed. Me and Sam were then reunited and the darkness was gone from this world.

Olly Dammer (10)

Craigowl Primary School, Dundee

Cuddles The Hero Saves The Day

Dear Diary,

My name is Cuddles. I went to the zoo one day and I saw a cute, cuddly animal. Then I went to the tiger cage but a baby tiger was stolen by a badger and I was sad. I never gave up and started to look and then I saw Baily Bunny. I said to Baily, "Have you seen my badger?" She said no but told me to look in the woods.

I looked in the woods and found a little cottage and saw Kali Cat. I said, "Kali Cat, have you seen my badger?"

"Yes, I have seen him in the hole in Sunshine Avenue."

She gave me the address of 29 Sunshine Corner.

"Thank you, Kali Cat."

"You're welcome," she said.

"Ah, I found you, Badger!"

"Oh no, I'm running away."

"Well, I have got you now."

"No!"

"Where is my baby tiger?"
"There you go!"
I then put the tiny baby tiger back in the zoo.

Gabriella Lettice (10)

Craigowl Primary School, Dundee

My Story

Dear Diary,

Can you believe what happened to me yesterday? I was just on a normal trip to my local library. I was picking up my favourite books and then when I got back to my house my horrid parents were shouting at me. All I want to do is go to school but my parents won't let me.

Lying in my bed and thinking about what it would be like to go to school, I realised I'd had enough and climbed out of the window. I looked up to see all the stars doing cartwheels on my roof and I started to head off when I heard, "Matilda, you awful girl!" I jumped back into my bed as quick as a flash and then my dad confronted me and said, "If you want to go to school you can go to school!" He laughed but I was very happy and putting my first blazer on felt amazing!

Mia Burgess (11)

Craigowl Primary School, Dundee

Darkness

Dear Diary,

Yesterday was so bizarre which is why I am in a hospital bed. Let me explain... I was in my room when I heard banging from my wall and I went to see what it was. I then heard it again so I decided to get a hammer from Dad's shed and I knew Dad wouldn't be happy about this but I had to find out what it was! A few minutes later I had the hammer and it was heavy! I started smashing the wall and then I saw a glimpse of what was inside... a door! My heart was saying, "Go, go, go!" but my head was saying, "What are you doing? Don't do it!" I was split... Because I was so curious I decided to go in. When I got in it stunk and then suddenly I heard footsteps and then I heard a big bang and everything went dark...

Aimee Slade (11)
Craigowl Primary School, Dundee

The Day I Was All Over The Place

Dear Diary,

When I came home today my mum said that my dad was in hospital. I was so sad. After tea my mum said, "Let's call Dad."

I said, "Okay."

We called him and he said that he was feeling fine and then we went down to drop his laptop off. Later my mum had to pick him up. My brother was hyper and started laughing like mad. He was hanging out of the window so I joined in. After that we went to Domino's. At half-past ten we got home and gobbled down some pizza and chugged Coke. I was so glad I was home. Then we had a disco with my friends and danced to some funny songs. We were dying with laughter and it was so funny and so weird.

When my parents walked in though I was so embarrassed.

Ellis Baird (10)

Craigowl Primary School, Dundee

A Day In The Life Of A Piece Of Paper

Dear Diary,

A big kid called Bob picked his nose and wiped it on me. Instead of doing his work he ate Cheetos and wiped his cheesy, snotty fingers on me! The teacher screeched at him and so he tried writing as hard as he could. I was in a lot of pain but only all of the other pieces of paper could hear me. Then a big hairy kid farted and it smelled. He spelt his name wrong and put the wrong date. After he was done that he doodled on me. The teacher got angry again. He also got angry because the teacher shouted at him so he knocked his water bottle and spilled it all over me! No one saw that I was crying. He then crumpled me up and threw me across the room and I got thrown back. Then Bob doodled on me again.

Cami McNicoll (11)
Craigowl Primary School, Dundee

Teddy's Diary

Dear Diary,

Hi, it's Teddy again. Yesterday I was so annoyed, let me explain... Okay, so I get squeezed a lot and my owner Holly is always getting dirty. She even shoved me in dog poo once! I hate Holly! Yesterday I tried telling her to stop getting me dirty but while I was saying this she put me in mud and I got it in my mouth! Yuck! When we got home I was so glad that Holly's mum was home because she put me in the washing machine and I was happy. When I was dry I wanted to stop her from getting me dirty so I took her hand and took her to a mud pit and I threw her in for revenge. Hehehe. I mean, what else could I do?
From Teddy.

Willow Jefferson (10)

Craigowl Primary School, Dundee

Tim Stops Bullying

Dear Diary,

My name is Tim and I go to Witson Primary School. I am ten years old and I get bullied. I get shoved about and food is taken off me. Once they even punched me! It's the worst feeling ever when you get bullied! Honestly I do nothing to deserve it, so why do they do it? Yesterday I was sick of it and I wanted to stick up for myself but I couldn't. This morning though I ate my porridge and was ready to stand up for myself. I got to school and the bullies were ready to have a go and I said, "Why do you do this to me?" Then I screamed, "Just stop it!" Guess what? They did. They stopped! Stop bullying!

Maisie O'Leary (11)
Craigowl Primary School, Dundee

The Story Of Hogtorts

Dear Diary,

It was dark and quiet at Hogtorts. Walter Potter and his friends Hermione Rangers and Ronald Peesly were sneaking into the kitchen. Just then I swooped and stopped the so did Severous Snake. Then I went to see Mrs Mgontogal on her trip with Hufflenuff at Edinbore Castle in Scotpond. I used a spell to get there. The whole of Gryftdoor were sad and Slytherbin were angry and Rovingclaw were happy. My favourite student ever was Pom Riddle who was Lord Baldermort. He turned evil so me, Sirus Wack and Professor Wolf killed him. My second favourite student: Winny Weasly.

Thanks for listening,

Albus Bumbledore.

Cody Ogilvie (11)

Craigowl Primary School, Dundee

Pepsi Man Saves Pepsi World

Dear Diary,

I'm Pepsi Man, protector of Pepsi World until Coca-Cola attacked Pepsi World. My mission was to stop them. I threw Pepsi cans at them and my sidekick Fanta Man was building a Coke and Mentos bomb. Eventually two other drinks joined, Dr Pepper Man and Sprite Man joined in. Sprite Man joined Coke and Dr Pepper Man joined us. Fanta Man said the bomb was finished so we jumped into the Pepsi mobile and we threw the bomb and took off. The war was finally over and we had a big Coke can clean up on our hands.

Pepsi Man.

Joey Rooney (10)

Craigowl Primary School, Dundee

Space Dog

Dear Diary,

My name is Space Dog. I have always wanted to be an astronaut and to go into space. When I was a little puppy my mum and dad passed away and I was adopted by a nice and healthy family and they took very good care of me. Then they adopted a little pup and it was like they forgot about me. Then they gave me away and I figured out that the people who adopted me for the second time were astronauts. When they were going to space I jumped on the rocket and we made it to space and we landed on the moon.

Kyan Bell (10)
Craigowl Primary School, Dundee

The Diabolical Diary Of The €20 Note

Dear Diary,

My life is hard! Every day I'm being passed smudged and scratched. I didn't really mind until one day I was taken out of the bank and was torn apart by a baby! They took me home and tried glueing me back together... It hurt and I cried for help but nobody heard me! Thankfully I got fixed but then I got a massive scar down my face. I was then taken to the bank once again to continue my rough life.

Kenneth Rattray (11)

Craigowl Primary School, Dundee

Cat Heroes

Dear Diary,

We were normal cats in our garden until we got struck by lightning. We felt scared until we felt good and we had superpowers. Then we felt happy that we were alright.

Tegan Heenan (11)

Craigowl Primary School, Dundee

The Catalytic Cause Of The Teddy Bear

Dear Diary,

My identity is a mystery and shall remain a mystery. I was a happy toy who played with her owner. She loved me to bits. A few months after she got me, she got a dog and it was obvious that she loved it more than me.

After she played with the dog it came over to me and sniffed me before tearing me up. The pain was unbearable and the dog was a demon sent from Hell. As my owner observed me lying there, torn apart, she declared that she didn't want me anymore and then threw a tantrum and put me back in the claw machine as someone might want me. How could she do this to me? The place I was in was very quiet and the only friend I had had backstabbed me.

I was just sat there withered, dismantled and solitary, wishing I could let all of the emotions out of me, I was furious and betrayed and then suddenly a kid came. He looked like he was about ten. He came up to the claw machine that I was in and took me...

Sidiki Saho (9)

E-ACT Blackley Academy, Blackley

A Normal Day In My Life

Dear Diary,

Every morning I get used for work. Every day I'm so bored. Every day kids do bottle flips on me. I really want to tell them my true feelings but I can't. They get their books out and start learning and when they don't know something they tap their fingers on me and draw on me. I think it's just a waste and a silly idea.

After school I get cleaned more than I ever have and then later the kids go on a break. I think it's because the teacher yells, "Break time!"

When they leave I feel so ecstatic to have a break and I get even more excited when it is the end of the day and the kids get a new toy. I get all sad when they lean on me and I get damaged and I move around all day. I'm still fuming because of this. There's nothing more exciting though than when the kids leave for home. I get as excited as a puppy being adopted and even more giddy than when I was first bought.

At home time I get depressed because I'm used like a coat hook. All the coats and bags are thrown on me and stuff is taken off and I no longer feel any pressure in this so-called danger zone. Don't worry, I named it this so there's nothing to worry about!

I hate Fridays because they sing a French song and bang their hands on me until I feel like collapsing into millions of pieces. After French I cry for days and days. I try to sleep but all the kids are chatting and talking and whispering. They're all chatterboxes and my owner is a school teacher sometimes.

Anyway, bye for now.

The school table.

Ellie Brady (9)

E-ACT Blackley Academy, Blackley

Ella's Diary

An extract

Dear Diary,

Do you know what it's like to be a refugee? Hi, my name's Ella and I've been living here a while now but let me tell you about my life...

A few months ago me and my family had to leave my hometown because of war. We lived in Dachau, Germany. We travelled from our home and found a boat. It was a long journey and we had to stop halfway. The sun went down and we had uncomfortable sleeping bags that we put on the grass. It was cold, wet and unpleasant. The next day we reached the squashed ship that everyone was trying to get on. The past I left behind in my country was like a ghost haunting me, it was gruesome.

After two days we arrived in London. I didn't have any food or drink and couldn't understand anyone. I felt like I was going to cry but I held back the tears and listened to Mother because she knew a few words. We had to stay hidden for a few days. The rain poured down and people cried in grief from losing their home.

We soon arrived at an apartment we were to stay in. My mother enrolled me into a new school and I had to go to a doctor in case I had a diagnosis. On my way to school, my dad took me in a rental van which was quite small. I was squashed, hungry and I needed a drink. My clothes were dirty. All the other girls had pretty shoes and clothes. I couldn't speak to anyone because I didn't understand anyone. However, the teacher was nice and they found me a translator. Now I have two friends called Coco and Auroura who are a comfort to me...

Henrmy Rashidi (10)
E-ACT Blackley Academy, Blackley

A Rough Day

An extract

Dear Diary,

Today was rough! The whole week was rough! The last few months had been rough! First, the war, leaving Dad behind and now I have to go to this new school. I shouldn't complain though; six hours of learning is better than days of sailing on a raft that could barely fit ten people. I hope Dad is okay. Mum keeps trying to reassure me that she is safe but I really think she is trying to reassure herself. My new school is nothing like my old one. The classroom is bigger. The desks are different and I have to sit next to a girl called Clarrissa. She talks a lot and is always staring. For some reason he books her geography book vertically in the table, using it as a separator. I don't mind though because I never really look around. I don't join in when we do PE because I don't know what to do; it looks boring anyhow.

At the end of the day some boy ran up to me and handed me an orange. After some hesitation, I took it as I knew I would be hungry at home. When I got back to the temporary accommodation we had been given, I showed my mother the orange and she looked pleased. "Ah, I see," she said with a smirk on her face, "making friends already?"

"I wouldn't exactly call them a friend!"

I was about to sit on our couch as I didn't have a bed because we couldn't afford a mattress so we all slept on this old leather couch that came with the room. By we all I mean my mother, me and my younger sister Mia...

Ula Markeviciute (10)
E-ACT Blackley Academy, Blackley

Ahmet's Diary

An extract

Dear Diary,

I see all my friends at school have a book to write and I want to fit in. I'm going to tell you about my journey.

1: The Decision... I was in my room chomping away at my favourite chocolate bar while watching my favourite show when suddenly... bang! There was a loud eruption just outside our house and people were crying. There was blood everywhere. I was deeply dead when I saw my dad lying on the floor unconscious. Just then some strangers ran into my room and put me in a strange van. I was glad to see my mum and sister there. Me and my mum comforted me and said, "These nice men will help." A few hours later, I found myself in a boat. The sky was crying and the clouds were angry. I was scared when the thunderbolt landed just two inches away from the boat. Luckily I could swim but my sister Azzi and my mum couldn't. I stayed next to them the whole ride Finally my mam who was shivering with fear helped me so we could get out of the huge boat.

2: A Temporary Service... We were finally there. After approximately six hours of sailing, we were escorted to an apartment. A drowsy one though. It had no windows and no light and spiders everywhere. It had only one room. The day was as warm as an oven on full heat. The night was as warm as a pile of coal. My mum complained to the lord that we couldn't survive this and then he just lost and started to scream at my mum like a wild bull...

Fatima Ceesay (10)
E-ACT Blackley Academy, Blackley

My Week

Dear Diary,

What a week I had! Last week, when I woke up on my chair as normal, I thought it would be a normal day but oh no, it was far from normal! It was chaos. At first I could distinguish the president's voice. It was sort of an angry tone. It was 1781, in Yorktown, and someone wandered into the room and his partner I guess you could say said, "Do you have an idea, these British troops are invading like a flock of birds!"

"Young man, we need to work together if we want to see daylight again!"

He swooped on me, I was going to be a nervous wreck! He sped through his poor troops. "If you would like to live another day I'd suggest you don't be a chicken and fight for your country!"

They were there. Wow! All the troops were amazing in battle. They were so brave. Just like a bear. It was stress-inducing, heart racing and blood pumping. I definitely needed a bath after. Everyone got some scars but hey, you win some and lose some. The British did a few kills but couldn't beat our troops... we won! Everyone nearly got shot at least once but we won!

We had a big celebration. There were so many coats of all different colours and there were flowers.

Suddenly my president resigned and someone named John Adams was soon running for president. I have a new owner now and I am back in control.

See you soon,

The used coat of George Washington.

Oliwia Zaniewska (9)
E-ACT Blackley Academy, Blackley

Coco's Diary

An extract

Dear Diary,

My family and I had to come to England to be safe. On our horrifying and scary journey, we were left with no food or water but we had to go on and took two whole years to escape from danger. Brother was crying and scared because we had to leave Grandma behind. Soon enough we arrived at her new house, we were so relieved that she was finally safe. All we were thinking about was Grandma. Dad, Brother, Mum and I went to the supermarket, Dad was talking to a refugee like us. He said something about a school. The next day we went to apply for the school. A minute later, they said I got a place. We were so happy and they also gave me my own translator who could help me speak English and who spoke my language. On my first day of starting, it felt weird as everybody was stopping and staring. I hoped my future was brighter than a shiny star in the night sky. Things though that I had ran away from, came back to haunt me in the darkness.

That day I came back to an empty, dirty, silent house. I went to my bedroom and I felt anxious and abandoned, dull and depressed. I didn't know what to do.

The blanket of dark hung over me and the bedroom gave me flashbacks of my country and the war. It got me thinking what would be happening if I was still there. I looked out of the window and it was raining heavily and still my parents hadn't come home...

Aaliyah Majeed Mcdermott (10)
E-ACT Blackley Academy, Blackley

Aria's Diary

An extract

Dear Diary,

I am Aria, I came over to England last month. The time getting over here in the van was vile. We were crammed together like sardines in a can. We had to leave everything behind: our grandparents and pets, we couldn't even call them since Mum's phone was lost in the van. There was no fresh food in the van and even worse, no drinks at all. It was horrible, I hated every second of it!

After two days of travelling from Syria, we arrived in England. We were starving when we got to the refugee camp. The line went on and on. One young boy had a fresh hot sandwich, yummy. I was so jealous. I thought we would be in the line for eternity. However, we got to the front fairly quickly thinking about it. Maybe it went fast because I fell asleep in Dad's arms.

After a week or so Mum found a house for us. The weather was dull so everyone's mood was awful all week.

Soon it was my first day at school in England. As I walked into class my soul left my body. I couldn't understand my teacher! Walking to my class I couldn't focus on finding my name printed on a laminated piece of paper telling me where to sit because the words just didn't look normal. I was terrified. "Will I ever get an education?" I asked myself, tears filling my eyes...

Lola Jade Hughes (10)
E-ACT Blackley Academy, Blackley

Aura's Diary

Dear Diary,

Hello, my name is Aura and this is my story... I used to live in Flossenburg, Germany and there was a terrible war. The journey to England began...

The boat road to England was excruciatingly cold and damp. I was so hungry and stayed quiet until we arrived.

The house we stayed in was cold and scary but I powered through and got some sleep. I went to somewhere called a school and the place was different. It had different food, they wore different clothes and spoke different words.

I walked in and sat down. I stayed silent. The teacher started speaking and the words were jumbled.

I was so scared and then I met a lovely lady called Rhea and finally some words came I could understand. She taught me some English words like Aura and hello.

On the playground I shivered as the sky cried tears of depression and sadness. Then a familiar face came and it was Mum. I jumped up and down and we went home. Tomorrow would be another day.

Dear Diary,

I'm feeling much better now. I made new friends called Ella and Coco and they are refugees from Flossenburg like me so it's easy to speak and we will practise English tomorrow. Anyways, tomorrow is a new day and I'm signing off.

Aura.

Faith L Wilson (10)

E-ACT Blackley Academy, Blackley

The Spectacular Spider-Man

An extract

Dear Diary,

What an amazing day! A few summers ago I was playing Spider-Man on the PS4 when I got to the boss level. The boss' name was Wilson Fisk and people called him Fisk for short. I was having fun webbing him up and doing combos on him when a cut scene came up. In the middle of the cut scene, Fisk has a remote with buttons on it and he pressed the teleport one and it teleported me inside the game. It was as scary as a lion about to attack you. I didn't know what to do and then I felt something tight wrapped around my wrists. They were web shooters. The web shooters weren't the only things I had, I had a whole suit too. I knew what I had to do, I had to fight him. First I shot my webs at him and he fell to the ground. When he fell I told the police and they took him to the Raft (special jail).

Kaboom! I defeated the lizard. *Pow!* I defeated Shocker. I defeated Taskmaster. There was one more villain left to fight... He was the biggest of them all. He was the baddest of them all. Worst of all, he was my boss! His name was Dr Octavius. He changed his name to Doc Oc and I went to fight him. I had to fight him, not only for his safety but for the entire city of Manchester...

Yahya Khan (9)
E-ACT Blackley Academy, Blackley

The Strawberry Sweetie

Dear Diary,

I'm truly sorry I have not been in touch for so long. I've had a terrible year. It's been heartbreaking. It started when all my friends finished Strawberry School so me, Jolly and Tasty were heading back from school and then out of nowhere we all heard a noise and rushed over to see what it was about. We regretted it ever since. There are so many words to describe it...

The humans had found us and they wanted to eat us! It was official, it was war. the humans were stronger but only a few of our families managed to survive. They completely destroyed our home! We had to make a run for it and I became a refugee. Who could have thought this could happen to Strawberry Farm? My home and favourite place in the world. It was like a wave of tears rolling down my face. I felt so mad I felt like I could cut through the humans but then I realised that not all humans were bad.

Then it hit me, I knew exactly what to do. I put my plan into action and I went back to my home to get a potion and then we made another potion.

The humans found us again. We surrounded them and we wouldn't stop apologising. They helped us rebuild the farm and I will see you tomorrow.

Parisa Halliru (9)
E-ACT Blackley Academy, Blackley

A Day In The Life Of An Ancient Greek Slave

Dear Diary,

What a disastrous hell of a day! You won't believe what happened! I feel exhausted. Will I get treated better one day? I miss my family!

It all began at 6am. Sir stomped in saying I had a date. He said I had to clean the house from top to bottom. I said okay and I cleaned like he said. Afterwards he came back in with some crops and he dropped all his crops! I felt like screaming but I held it in!

At lunchtime my boss got his 1000 Euros and he asked me to come and cook him some food. I said okay and I cooked some crop soup. I cooked the soup for twenty minutes and she came at 1:30. He didn't tell me she was allergic though! While I was cleaning the pots, she had some and she started to get bruises and her throat was swelling up.

Sir yelled, "Call a medic!"

She got taken away by the ambulance and Sir was vicious. He said, "You're not eating today!"

I ran upstairs and I felt so alone. I wish I had enough money saved up to see my son and my wife who is also poorly.
Signing off now,
Slave 101.

Lily-Rae Jubbs (8)
E-ACT Blackley Academy, Blackley

Life As An Ancient Greek Slave

Dear Diary,

Today is full of despair! I feel worthless. Can I stop him before it's too late? Wait, wait, wait... Let me explain...

As soon as I woke up I was positive that today would be okay. But as you know, good can turn into bad. Unfortunately, the evening was different. Before bed, I was washing the dishes when I overheard my owner say, "She has enough money to be free and I can't let that happen." I knew I would feel like nothing but I really did feel like nothing. I have never felt so low since I was captured. I do everything for him and now I want to be free and it's a no!

I should calm down. I just wish I could stop him! Good night.

Aleena Halliru (8)
E-ACT Blackley Academy, Blackley

The Best Day Ever

Dear Diary,

Today has been one of the best days ever. I woke up in a good mood and I got up and it was brilliant. Will the same be said for tomorrow? How could I make it better?

It all started this morning, I went to work and my owner said I had the day off. I was thrilled. When I got home I told my family and they were happier than ever. We could finally spend some time together. We went for a walk but the more I think about it, it was a waste because I walked to work just for my owner to tell me I was off.

I wish this happened every day so it can always be peaceful and I can spend time with my family.

See you tomorrow,

Aaron.

Aaron Farrell (8)
E-ACT Blackley Academy, Blackley

My Interesting Day

Dear Diary,

I am the most happiest penguin in the world because I have a doughnut but one day I went to get my doughnut but it was long gone! I was really sad so then I got inside my car and then I started my adventure. I was very good at adventures. Driving for miles, I stopped to get some answers and then a penguin walked to me and he told me that there was a bunker inside a tall snow hill and I needed a jet pack. I didn't have one so I caught some crooks and I got £1,000,000! Then I got a jet pack and I found the snow hill and I saw penguin guards. They saw me and they were firing bullets and I dodged the bullets and I got a grenade! I threw the grenade and bang! The penguin guards were dead so I jumped on the deck and then there was a keypad. I guessed the code 'doughnut' and it was correct.

A penguin emperor sat on a throne by the side of a cage. In the cage was the doughnut! "You cannot get the doughnut!" he said.

I got a bazooka and I fired. Got it!

Oscar Salt (8)

Great Easton Primary School, Great Easton

The Hungry Life Of Super Cat

Dear Diary,

Today I did all the usual like fight the evil Joker Dog but the worst thing was, my owner Batman forgot to feed me! I was so hungry but my owner was out so I called him on the cat phone and guess what? He was at Commissioner Gordon's house. I got into my Catmobile and went over. Finally, I got my food!

"Roar!" It was Joker Dog! He was in a giant robot. I couldn't do it alone. I had to call the rest of the gang. The team got here. There is Superdog, Wonder Bunny, Green Kitten, Flash the Frog, Aquafish and Martian Fishunter. "We're here!" they said.

It was crazy. *Bang! Pew! Pow!* The Joker Dog was defeated. What a crazy day we had!

Eva Bailey (9)
Great Easton Primary School, Great Easton

The Speaking Aeroplane

Dear Diary,

I was so lonely in this cupboard. I was once just a plain, white, flat thing with all the other ones then on a Sunday morning a boy called Ethan picked me up and made me into a paper aeroplane. It was a bit scary when he threw me. I loved it though when Ethan put me on his bedside table and went to sleep. All was quiet and I was not myself around the other toys. If you decide to make a paper aeroplane, keep an eye on it and your other toys as they might be chatting away while you sleep!

Ethan Boevé (8)

Great Easton Primary School, Great Easton

Mermaid Friends

Dear Diary,

Something happened a few days ago. I went to the seaside and something strange happened. I turned into a mermaid! My two friends were the same as well as my puppy Chip. Me and my friends started swimming when we saw something... it was a shark! "Swim! Go!" We swam as fast as we could. "Come on Camryn!" It suddenly became very shallow and we transformed back into humans. That was a very long day!

Camryn Mcintyre (8)

Great Easton Primary School, Great Easton

My Scary Adventure

Dear Diary,

Today was a scary day, it all started when I was casually driving and suddenly I saw a portal in the middle of the road. In the portal I saw a monster. It was black all over and had red, spiky horns. The monster grabbed me and suddenly I was in space. The monster then told me to go to Mars Bar which was in another galaxy!

Freddie (8)

Great Easton Primary School, Great Easton

An Awesome Day

Dear Diary,

Today I was having an awesome day travelling through time to the 1960s where I met James Bond in an action movie! I got his autograph and then I went home and went to bed dreaming of my day It was really awesome and for a second time I hope to travel to a different era!

Tobias Allen Williams (8)

Great Easton Primary School, Great Easton

Lost

Dear Diary,

Yesterday I was flying as high as a volcano when I got lost in the sky. Suddenly a heron dragon came and helped me down with her magic. At first I thought she would send me higher but she helped me get down so I thanked her and suddenly I was back to normal.

Riley Parker (8)

Great Easton Primary School, Great Easton

The Bad Day

Dear Diary,

I was sitting in the pouch when I got pulled out and got smudged on the whiteboard. I hated it in the classroom. I was so sick and sad. I wanted to die. Kids were playing with me and I was having a good day until I was of no more use.

George Luckin (8)

Great Easton Primary School, Great Easton

West Ham

Dear Diary,

Today was a great day. I scored three goals playing football for West Ham. I played at the London Stadium and I was very happy. I then drove to the café with the team and we had a Fanta.

Kyle Morris (8)

Great Easton Primary School, Great Easton

A Mermaid On A Desert Island

Dear Diary,

Hey, I saw three children in a boat. They came and shoved a big blue play stick thing into the ground. They went inside it. I looked at them and I noticed they didn't have a scaley tail like me. What could they be? They had legs and toes, I didn't have those! Were they human? Do you think they heard me? They did hear me! I jumped back into the sea and I swam to my actual home. I rushed in and my mum said, "Hey, are you hurt?"

"No, the humans are destroying my desert island!"

"Who?" Mum asked.

"Three humans!" I yelled.

My mum locked me in the room for safety and she spread the word around Atlantis. When? How? Why? I wasn't allowed out but I sneaked out and I saw three children on the floor and when I went on land I screamed because I had turned into a human. This woke them up and I told them my name. They told me theirs: Ben, Myda and Chloe. Soon we were friends.

Jessica Ryder (8)
St John's CE Primary School, Keele

The Fabulous Birthday

Dear Diary,

I woke up at 7'clock, it was my birthday. I was also going to a party, it was Soren's party. I was soon at the swimming party and after that I went home and I got a present and it was a foal. A foal is a baby horse and I screamed with happiness.

I was so happy that I decided to go to the supermarket to get materials to make a shed for the foal. When we go all of the materials me and my my dad went home and I named my horse. "I will call her Rose, or Kiry, or Ninu!"

"No, how about Luna, Hop or Shorlit?"

We decided to call her Rose and after a month I was riding her. She is so beautiful. She is multicoloured and she had black hair.

We once did a competition and they asked me my name and I said, "My name is Isabella."

"Okay," they said, "you may go in."

After the competition, they decided the winner and I had won!

Ashleigh McKinson (8)
St John's CE Primary School, Keele

The Men In Black

Dear Diary,

Today I woke up in my house and then went on my motorbike. I went to my office and did some spy work. My boss called me and said there were aliens in a lifeboat and we needed to get the speedboat and chase them because they had stolen a diamond.

I rushed to the speed boat and chased them down and I put them in the slammer.

I then got back on th motorbike and saw aliens in a hot-air balloon. I waited to see what would happen. A new officer who was a junior agent came and we went on admission. There was this guy named Farmer and he was a top suspect because an alien had taken over his body.

We found him and he dashed into his UFO. When we saw his alien form we both thought he looked hideous. He was a giant cockroach and we blasted him to the floor. He came back and I got my booster and shot but it came back to life again...

William Bryan (8)
St John's CE Primary School, Keele

The Diary Of The Bottom Of A Shoe

Dear Diary,

What a day I had! First someone put me on. We went to the park and my owner went on the monkey bars and let go of the rubber mat on a hot day. I thought it burnt so, so much. What next? The dumpster chewing gum pit! When we went a day ago it went fine but often it doesn't go well because one day I stood on one and it was a mint one. I didn't think they would put me on again but, uh-oh, where next? The shop! I thought this would be okay until I saw a sign about being careful of a wet floor and then my owner walked closer to it and we fell! Probably because she's clumsy! Anyways, I went through a painful day that day. Wait, that wasn't the end! What next? London. Okay, nothing could go wrong but when we got there, I was eaten by a dog! It was a hard day!

Emily Bucknall (8)

St John's CE Primary School, Keele

A Fish Called Jefrey Bagle

Dear Diary,

Today Mum Lady gave me some magnificent food (fish food) and Dad Man put me in the washer thing and washed my fantastic ocean. I then met a beautiful lady called Shimmer. I also met a new boy called Berik. I also regretted being so mean earlier to my brother called Bob. Oh, speaking of names, I'm called Jefrey Bagle. I love adventures and today was an adventure. While Mum Lady was busy watching Indiana Jones, I was about to eat some fish food when Bob ate it all! Can you believe that? I love Shimmer though, she is cool. Back to my adventure, I went to my underwater castle and I loved it. I then saw some fish food and went to grab it but it was on a shelf in front of the window. I then fell out of the window and ended up in a... pond!

Till next time!

Elliot Deaville (8)
St John's CE Primary School, Keele

A Day In The Life Of A Gaming Controller

Dear Diary,

Today I woke up glowing. Well, just on my head. Suspiciously there was a 3D cuboid with some sort of symbol as me. Mmmm, maybe we were connected? I was picked up. Why was he poking me? It made me scared that he might... lose! I knew what would happen next... Ouch! I got thrown for about five minutes. One day he would learn his lesson the hard way and when he did, I would be sad.

I hated when he came in with crisps like he did today. He got the dust all over me. One minute later, he got angry and threw me and as a result, my left stick broke and I immediately stopped glowing. I burst into tears but the cuboid was still glowing...

Charlie Boulton (9)

St John's CE Primary School, Keele

A Diary Of A Secret Birthday

Dear Diary,

I woke up this morning and it was a beautiful day. I got ready in my leopard print skirt and T-shirt. Then I went over to my mum and woke her up. She reminded me about Ashleigh McKinan's birthday party. Then we had some breakfast which was porridge and I wrapped up a present, which was a 'make your own birdhouse'. Then me and dad got into the car and went to the party.

I was with Freya and Alice. We played games. Alice went first but I won. Then we went to the play area. Alice went inside but I stayed out and then I went and had some cake. I also had a chocolate lolly. I had an incredible day. I loved it!

Evelyn Rose Kamarauskas (8)

St John's CE Primary School, Keele

The Story Of Louise Hamilton

Dear Diary,

I got up and got ready for my dream day. I was so excited for this day. I got in my car and drove off to the track. I saw the F1 car and had flashbacks of how to drive it. I got in the F1 car and drove out to the track.

I went to the starting line and I revved the engine and warmed the tyres. I was scared but I was ready for it.

3, 2, 1... go! I went 100mph. I zoomed around the track and I slowed down but my engine blew! I stepped on the throttle and it was not going much faster. I could not turn and I crashed. Luckily I got out of the car just in time because the car was burning. I got injured but I survived.

Callum Mckinon (8)

St John's CE Primary School, Keele

The Kid Spy

Dear Diary,

At night I broke out of the house and found my target. I ran as fast as a cheetah and I caught him. His name was Jack. He was a very incredibly skilled boy and when he saw me he ran and ran until he was gone.

Attempt one was a failure. I made a new plan. First I needed to get some hard metal then I needed to use the right technology to make a tracking device. I sneaked into the garage and stole some metal and made it.

The next day I found him and I threw a tracking device and followed him. I was sneaky so he didn't notice me. Finally, I captured him.

Erdem Misirli (7)
St John's CE Primary School, Keele

The Mario Day

Dear Diary,

Today I was in excitement. It was Mario Day, my birthday. It was exciting and I got a super star, I loved it! I got a super mushrooms and fire power and I also got a pet called Yoshi. I put my pet Yoshi into my house. My pet Yoshi and my brother Luigi then got captured! I set off through the acorn plains and the desert valley and finally arrived at the castle. I was being attacked. *Argh!* A hammersuit appeared. *Boom, boom, squash!*

In the end, my brother Luigi and my pet Yoshi were saved by Toad.

Harrison Currie (7)
St John's CE Primary School, Keele

Lord Voldemort

Dear Diary,

It is Voldemort, from the Dark Mark here. Wait, why am I being kind? I'm evil! I'm doing an evil laugh. Mwahaha! Anyway, let's get on with it. I did have a go at Harry but those pesky friends of his totally ruined my plans. Oh they will pay with big consequences! Okay, let's get on with this... So, I had a talk with the Death Eaters and they never listen. I told them to set a trap for the boy but then silly Dumbledore helped this time. Suddenly the Dementors appeared and Harry was lucky again!

Nawfal Shivji (8)

St John's CE Primary School, Keele

The Story Of Kirby

Dear Diary,

Today some weirdo was controlling me with a strange device, a gaming controller! They were making me eat some random things! I was then forced to fight a gigantic gorilla and the person that was controlling me made me defeat him. I was then forced to fight a pineapple. I found him easier to defeat. Then the gorilla came back one last time and after that I had to fight a lion. It took me hours and hours but finally I did it. Finally I completed the game.

Solomon Karimi (8)

St John's CE Primary School, Keele

My Star Concert

Dear Diary,

Hello, I'm Ariana Grande and today I had the most exciting day of the year. My star concert, yes, that's right! I flew all the way from LA to Miami and we started setting up for my special day at the Star Concert Theatre. You never guess who invited me... Billie Eilish! Oh, of course I can't forget my beautiful dog Lola (she's very giddy but I just love her energy!) Honestly, Lola won't stop jumping up and messing with my violet hair.

It was finally time, 6pm at night and I sang my first song. I then noticed Neymar was in the crowd. I was so excited that I got a bit too close to the end of the stage and accidentally fell off - ouch! I wondered if my leg would be okay, luckily I hadn't broken any bones but I did have to go to the hospital. My leg was aching from the fall and I thought I had lost my dog! At least I hadn't lost my mind!

As soon as I got home, Lola jumped up and licked my face which was so relieving as I thought she was lost. I'm really glad though that I met Billie Eilish and Neymar and... well, me! Do you want to be a singer when you're older?

Florence Penney (9)
St Mary's CE Primary School, Greenfield

The Day Of Adventure

Dear Diary,

Today I had the best day ever! I was just doing my job when a massive hand picked me up and then my family as well and we got dropped down a huge hole. Me and the children were going crazy back there when, out of nowhere, my wife and Clair appeared. Clair said, "You look like you need some help!" She opened her lid and glued our hands and we climbed up the steep mountain. Suddenly it started shaking and we landed in a pile of yuck. Me and my family finally climbed out of the tip and we fell to the floor every time someone walked past.

Suddenly, Pip, Podly, Patric and Persy all shouted, "No!" really loudly.

I turned around and Timmy was riding a huge monster. We ran with our tiny feet as fast as we could and I jumped onto the monster and my family followed me. I could feel the soft wind on my freezing feet as it dropped us off at the massive mountain pot.

We ran inside with hope and joy after climbing the

mountain, slithering in a bony thing and seeing a poster reading: 'Here is a dinosaur!' I sure had a good sleep that day!

Scarlett Gunton (9)

St Mary's CE Primary School, Greenfield

Mission Impossible

Dear Diary,

Today I was chased by an assassin who was in a Hummer whilst I was handcuffed to Grace who tried to kill me multiple times and who was an excellent pickpocketer. We were in an excellent Fiat 500 and that thing was battered by the time we got out. We were crashing left and right. Did I mention Grace was an excellent pickpocketer? She was also a terrible driver. The assassin nearly hit us but I pulled out the oldest trick in the book and drove backwards onto a railway line. Did I mention Grace has tried to kill me multiple times? Make that a lot of times!

Our car was stuck on the tracks and she tied the handcuffs to the wheel and when the train came I shot out of the car like a bullet as I saw it come past. Then I thought about the key that Gabriel had and I was curious as to what it opened. At least the Fiat was a safe car because behind it I saw a Ferrari Spider and a man. I drove that thing anyway and Benji was giving me directions which came in handy as it was my first time in Venice. Hmmm, I wondered if I would ever find the key...

Hayden Moss (9)

St Mary's CE Primary School, Greenfield

My Insane Day

Dear Diary,

Today was insane! I fought Batsy again, this time I retreated but next time I'd win as I was Tricolour Twister. Before I get into too much detail, I just want to say that I fought well. Now that stupid Batman is always one step ahead of me so yesterday I stole a scientist from Wayne Tower and in the intensity of it all, he answered every question I asked him with an honest answer. "Where's Batman? What's his greatest weapon?" You should have seen his face, Diary. I sat him in a metal chair and told him to get to work with inventing me something amazing, extreme, something... evil! Earlier in the day Batman had said in a stiff voice, "Stop in your tracks, Joker!" I mean, can't a man just shut up? Anyway, finally the scientist finished and gave me a box of plastic chattering teeth. I wound one up and threw it. I then watched as it exploded. Now I was going to have some fun...

Theodore Gifford-Dixon (9)
St Mary's CE Primary School, Greenfield

Ruby The Rubber And Her Adventure

Dear Diary,

Today was the worst day ever. I woke up to Polly the Pencil poking me so now I have a hole in my hip. The teacher told the class we were going outside for art to draw trees and flowers. But this thing picked me up and took me with her. After everyone finished drawing they got to play tig. Guess what? My owner dropped me and ran off! When they were lining up she didn't even bother to get me inside and it started raining heavily. I jumped up and I fell off the bench. After two hours of me lying there, the gates opened. *Freedom*, I thought. Every time I tried to stand up though I got stood on.

After the gates closed again, I felt disappointed and I didn't get out.

Finally, Mr Beckwith found me and took me inside. He then gave me to Miss Smith.

Lucy Hill (9)

St Mary's CE Primary School, Greenfield

London Escape

Dear Diary,

This morning I woke up on a metal rod. It really hurt! On my first try I failed and the same goes for my second. Finally, on my 79th try I got off. Suddenly a man came. He screamed and I screamed. He screamed and I screamed. He screamed and I punched him. He fell over but I didn't care. I ran off and up the stairs into the... dinosaur section! I walked carefully around the aisles until another human came and I grabbed the bone of a tyrannosaurus and, well, what can I say? I ran and swung... *thump!* They fell and I ran off down some more stairs. I then saw a big dinosaur called Doppy. I think that's what it read! I asked for directions. She said, "The door is behind you!"

"Thanks," I said.

But as soon as I opened the door...

Bill Southall (9)
St Mary's CE Primary School, Greenfield

Cookie In A Cage

Dear Diary,

It is Monday and clearly I have got Mondayitis! I may have bit Jessica but my teeth were hurting and the pain wouldn't stop so I find biting stuff helps but Jessica normally won't let me bite anything. There is Emma, Jessica's mummy and also Harry her brother. When I bite someone Emma screams and shouts at me and whenever I bite something Jessica takes it off me and she always takes my chew off me but it is mine! She says it's because it's a choking hazard! When I bite her she shoves a teddy in my face! I may have earlier jumped on the bed and bitten Jessica's face but then when I'm put in my cage I don't like it. I do get all my toys but then they shut the door and say I need a nap. They then leave the room but I am not tired!

Jessica Whiteley (9)

St Mary's CE Primary School, Greenfield

Ribbon Life

Dear Diary,

Today was possibly the worst day ever. It was horrible! I know what you're thinking, why would such a beautiful ribbon have such a horrible day? Well, this is how it started...

It started at school (as normal) I was just doing my job and then a giant hand came in and grabbed me. Then before I could do anything I was tied to a gate and I was so angry. Then I accidentally fell off and I felt so sad and lonely that I was away from my family. I tried to get back inside but as soon as I was about to give up trying, someone picked me up and I was as happy as a dog playing. The person took me into their house and put me on a desk and I made a lot of new friends like a glue stick and I even saw my sister.

Nina Buckley (9)
St Mary's CE Primary School, Greenfield

The Magical Sky Islands

Dear Diary,

Today was an amazing day of exploring in the magical great sky islands. I was on an adventure to get off the islands when I found an unexplored cave. It was guarded by a soldier, an ancient robot with a sharp horn on its head that usually carried an iron sword. When I defeated it, I explored the cave and came to a large area of unexplored islands. After some exploring, I found a strange pillar on a large circle island. Out of curiosity, I went to examine it. An eye on it spotted me and the pillar transformed into a huge robot made out of cubes.

I soon found out two things: first you have to hit the eye and second it is deadly. I did some damage but I soon had to retreat...

Lochlan Holland (9)

St Mary's CE Primary School, Greenfield

The Lonely Teddy Bear

Dear Diary,

Yesterday I was lonely because I fell on Jack's bed and his mum saw me there. What happened was, she put me in the attic because she thought that Jack was getting too old for a teddy. She put me in the attic! I do not like the attic! It is dark but the good thing was there was an old TV in there so I turned it on and I watched it for a little while. Then I found a game called Monopoly and I played that for a little while. I then found a mini trampoline and I bounced on it and made some friends called Dolly and Molly. Then we all bounced together and Jack heard something. He came up and found me and took me back to his room and, finally, I was home sweet home.

Summer Bowker (9)
St Mary's CE Primary School, Greenfield

The Kitchen Race

Dear Diary,
Today was the torment of the kitchen. To the side of me I saw a fellow toast as the white piece of felt went up. We went as fast as a treadmill. The first part was a blaze over the knives, through the roll of toilet paper and under the paper shreds. Then we had to face the hoomans! Papery was grabbed and drawn on so he was eliminated then it was over the hand, under the hand, around the hand. Suddenly I was grabbed and a bit of me was eaten but I kicked the hooman in the face and I jumped back into the tournament but it was too late as Pebbly Boy had won!

Nile Holland (9)
St Mary's CE Primary School, Greenfield

Cuddles The Teddy Bear

Dear Diary,

Yesterday was okay. I started off in Build-A-Bear and I was so flat. Suddenly a girl picked me to be her bear. I was so excited! OMG! It was the best feeling in the world! I got stuffed with stuffing and it felt so amazing to be 3D for once. Then the girl took me home and called me Mr Cuddles. She slept with me but then I fell down a gap in her bunk bed. It had cobwebs and it was so dusty. I was so cold. In the morning the girl found me and gave me a big hug. Then she dressed me in shoes and a dress and I now feel so professional!

Laura Ratcliff (9)

St Mary's CE Primary School, Greenfield

My Mission As A Bee

Dear Diary,

Today I had a new mission. I had to go out and scare people and steal crisps. I then buzzed away from the scene so nobody killed me and hid from all the people. I saw a robber and it was scary but I scared them away before they could hurt anybody. I scared the robber and then I had an ice cream for all my hard work. I also took some water but I didn't drink it because I could die if I did. I then did another mission. I helped a man cross the road and then I buzzed around a little more and saw a rocket for the first time!

Harry Bennett (9)

St Mary's CE Primary School, Greenfield

Dog Buds

Dear Diary,

Yesterday I went for a walk to Greenfield Park. I was playing with my ball and then Freddie threw my ball. I saw another dog and went over to him and his owner said, "This is Barney." Me and Barney played with the ball and Harry and Freddie played football for ages. Then I went home and had some tea and Harry and Freddie threw a ball for thirty minutes and I was so happy and joyful. Then me and Barney went to sleep because we were tired while Harry and Freddie played on the PlayStation all night long.

Freddie Taylor (9)

St Mary's CE Primary School, Greenfield

The Diary Of The Salmon

Dear Diary,

I was swimming down the river and then I got lost. Then I came across an oyster and he chased me. I managed to escape. Then I went hunting for a small silver fish called a roach. I spotted one and then I went to attack and it was so cool. I was the happiest fish alive. Then I did a fake fly before realising it was a fisherman and I escaped quickly. It was terrifying!

The next morning I felt tired and exhausted but I needed to get to the sea. I got there eventually and I saw all my friends.

Geoffrey Podmore (9)

St Mary's CE Primary School, Greenfield

Neymar Jr

Dear Diary,

Today I was getting ready to go to the match. I was with Mbappé and we were going out of the door. We then heard cheering and screaming. People were cheering! Some were booing! We started dancing. The second we started, I tackled people and I scored a goal.

After the match Mbappé came over to my place and we watched our match. We saw Ariana Grande and we wished we had seen her sooner. When it turned 10pm, Mbappé went home and I went to bed.

Darcey Fitzpatrick (9)
St Mary's CE Primary School, Greenfield

The Worst Two Days

Dear Diary,

Firstly I was hung on a washing line with a bunch of other pegs and clothes. Then it started to rain so they took all the clothes and pegs but left me outside! I thought that was quite brutal of them, especially when there was thunder and lightning. Well, it was quite a day out there! This morning though they finally realised I was still on the washing line and they took me in and locked me in a deep, dark cupboard and now here I am, writing this in the dark!

Freya Doxford (9)

St Mary's CE Primary School, Greenfield

A Yummy Treat

Dear Diary,

Today was amazing. I was compacted. I woke up in the bright light of the kitchen light and my journey began here... A strange thing suddenly grabbed me and put me in a sort of cooker and I felt warm. I started turning hard and it was unexpectedly uncomfortable. I was crispy! Then I got put into a waffle maker and I was then happily chomped up!

Enzo Bailey (9)

St Mary's CE Primary School, Greenfield

The Horsesome Diary Of A Pony

Dear Diary,

I was woken up this morning by Lola who was putting on my head collar and trying to usher me out of the stable. Yawn, I was so tired. Did I really need to be dragged off to a show at this time in the morning?

"Come on!" Lola begged and pleaded, pulling at the lead rope. She finally tempted me into the trailer with some sweets and we were off.

I began to feel nervous and no amount of excitement could match the fatigue I felt. The trailer then shuddered to a halt and I was led outside. The sight overwhelmed me. People, horses, and vehicles were bustling along and clip-clopping about.

My heart filled rapidly with a desire to join them and my tiredness was replaced with an immense feeling of ecstasy.

Lola unbolted the door and skipped into view. Her face was shining with glee. She was dressed in an immaculate shirt and jacket and a pair of spotless white jodhpurs.

Lola took me to a huge dressage arena and plaited my mane and tail. She then slid a polished saddle on my back and a shining bridle over my head. Lola mounted me and I strutted out into the crowds. I pranced here and there and did everything Lola told me to do. It was perfect. I was so proud. We were awarded a red rosette and bow and I got extra hugs from Lola at the end.

Now I'm back at home in my comfy stable bed at last.

From Shadow.

Lola Massarella (10)
St Nicholas CE Primary School, Reading

Olympics

Dear Diary,

Today I ran a whole 600m. Do you believe that, Diary? All the big stars were there like Mo Farah and Usain Bolt. I was so excited, imagine being at the Olympics. It is so cool!

First I watched my friend Ted run the 100m and 200m and he won twice! I couldn't believe it, he had beaten Usain Bolt! Take that Bolt! After that I met him at the Olympic Village and we talked for a bit. Then he needed to go and celebrate so I left him to it.

Two hours till the race kicked in, I started to worry. Would I win? Where would I come? Would I get a medal? Who knows but I was loving the Olympics so far.

One hour until the race. I walked to the track humming to the song 'I'm So Excited'. Then I saw Mo Farah and my mood swung dramatically.

One minute till the race and everyone had done their stretches and were at the starting position. The gun fired and we ran off. I was soon second behind Mo Farah and he started to slow so I took the opportunity and came in first! Wow! Before I knew it I had crossed the line and was ready to get my medal.

After that, I partied allnight. Bye, Diary, see you soon.

William Randles (10)

St Nicholas CE Primary School, Reading

The Day I Got Signed By Reading

Dear Diary,

Today I went to football training session at the Madejski Stadium in Reading. The training session was great! We played a few matches at the start then did more technical bits like dribbling to the cone and back. My favourite activity was the 3 vs 3 tournament because we won. The best coach was Jamie as he was very enthusiastic and funny and he even taught me the Maradonna.

At the end of training I had made loads of friends. I walked to the car with Dad and hopped in. Dad revved the engine and then Jamie tapped on the window and said Reading would like to sign me. I was over the moon when he said Reading would like to sign me. He offered me a contract and I said yes.

While I was signing the contract, some of the Reading players came to see me. They were my favourite players like Andy Carrol, Shane Long and

Jonathan Swift. I even met Sir John Madejski. Finally, I signed the contract and went home. Bye, Diary.

Adam Woodward (10)

St Nicholas CE Primary School, Reading

My Two Silver Medals

Dear Diary,

My name is Dhiya and today was the most stressful day I've ever had. I competed in London 2012 Olympics and I competed in gymnastics and I had done a floor and vault routine. For my floor routine my music was Super Maro Bros. Then it came time for my back tuck. Guess what? I landed it. The judges jumped up and started applauding me. A small smile emerged on my face as I presented to the judges and left.

As soon as I left, my points came up on the board... I was in first place! Next up was the vault, the scariest of all. They gave us a little break and then I continued. In my break I went on the trampoline to practise my half-turns, which is something you do over vault in a sideways handstand. It was my turn...3, 2, 1... go! Yes, I ended it with a stumble. I looked up at the points board, I had gone down to 2nd but that was fine because I still had two silver medals proudly displayed on my bedroom wall.

Love Dhiya.

Dhiya Singaravelan (10)
St Nicholas CE Primary School, Reading

The Horrendous Flight

Dear Diary,

Last night was a tough night on the aeroplane on the way to Hong Kong. I was sitting in the middle amongst my mum and brother and it was my worst experience on a plane. You would only understand if you were there.

I said I was in the middle which was probably the worst idea but it started off pretty well.

The first few hours was okay because we weren't tired yet and there was food to eat. Unfortunately, the worst came about three hours after dinner when my mum told us to sleep. I tried my best, I really did, but you should know how hard it was to go to the loo suddenly.

Afterwards, my brother, who is the heaviest person I know, had to sleep on my leg and lucky for him he could sleep but I couldn't due to normal situations. When we boarded, my leg was aching and I was so annoyed, grumpy, tired and it turned out that I only slept for thirty minutes.

Now I need to sleep, bye!

Gianne.

Gianne Hui (10)

St Nicholas CE Primary School, Reading

My Fantastic Day

Dear Diary,

Today was fantastic. I woke up bright and early. My owner put a bowl of food out for me and then we went for a walk. In the field I ran around and it felt amazing to be outdoors. I ran and chased lots of birds. When the walk ended I was a bit upset because I knew what was coming next. On the drive there I sat in the back seat scared about what could happen.

I hopped out of the car and the owner gave me a big hug. I was terrified as we were at the dog groomers. I could feel the cold breeze on my body. The man put me on the table and I looked down, I was 10,000 feet in the air. I looked back towards the man, he had scissors in his hand and I was shocked.

When I left the groomers my owner had come back and I was so happy. My owner said I looked very nice.

When we got home she gave me lots and lots of treats. What a day it has been.

Martha May Piggins (10)

St Nicholas CE Primary School, Reading

My Disco Party

Dear Diary,

Oh my goodness, what a day it has been! I had a disco party, can you believe it? It was so fun! Oh, and dearest Diary, guess what? My mum said I could have waffles for breakfast. They were so good. Yum!

After that me and my dad went to the village hall which was where the party was happening. The first thing that came to me was how big it was. It was gigantic. My dad said not to touch anything or do anything until every guest was here. This went on for a bit - boring!

When everyone finally arrived the lights were turned off and there was a DJ, lights and music. I had so much fun. I then sat down to eat. There was a massive cake in front of me. It was so strange. Then Mum jumped out of the cake and everyone sang happy birthday.

Next when every guest had gone we went home. It was the best day ever.

Thanks for talking, Lily.

Lily Rand (10)
St Nicholas CE Primary School, Reading

My Pink Concert

Dear Diary,

Today I went to my first concert and it was absolutely amazing. Me and my friends Jess, Isabell, Lisa and Louisa went to see Pink. I was so excited and nervous.

It took an hour to get to Hyde Park and it was so busy. There were over 10, 000 people and it was scary. It was my birthday and my mum bought us pizza and chips. Pink didn't come on until 9:30 so we had to wait hours and hours but it was still absolutely amazing.

Gwen Stefani was the support act and I did not know her but Mum did. I had two bags of sweets and they were yummy.

I loved watching Pink and I soon got a sugar rush. Pink sang some songs like 'Let's Get This Party Started' and 'Never Gonna Dance Again' and lots more. Eventually she closed the show with birthdays and I was picked to go on stage. It was fantastic!

Zoe Henderson (10)
St Nicholas CE Primary School, Reading

My Time At Centre Parcs

Dear Diary,

My weekend away was stress-filled but action-packed!

On Friday 23rd June, we left home at 10:30. Suddenly, two hours into our journey, the car engine overheated and seven hours later - call after call - we made it to Longleat.

The next day, we hired three bikes and we swam for two hours. It was so much fun! At 6pm, we had Mexican food for dinner and the humid climate made it feel so realistic. Then we went bowling - when finished, we walked back to our lodge. The next day we took the park's train to the Sports Plaza and participated in an hour of rock climbing. After that, we went to Starbucks and did field archery. We then finished and hoped that Friday wouldn't repeat itself.

The next day we got home safely and knew we had the best adventure possible.

Amelia Loader (10)

St Nicholas CE Primary School, Reading

My Football Journey

Dear Diary,

Today I woke up excited because I was going to play my football match. It happened every week on Saturday. I got changed into my football kit and slipped down the stairs to have my breakfast. After that I walked out of the house excited.

In the car I was nervous like I am every week before a match. It was like there were butterflies in my stomach.

After we arrived I got out of the car and I ran out onto the field. The team started the warm-up and the next thing I knew, it was kick-off.

After the match ended I had completed a hat-trick and I was about to walk to the car when a man in a Liverpool jacket strolled over. I support Liverpool so was delighted. He said, "Would you like to play for Liverpool?" I lit up with excitement.

From Noah.

Noah Westerling (10)

St Nicholas CE Primary School, Reading

Football Times

Dear Diary,

Today I woke up with my brothers and sisters in a bucket. It was very uncomfortable to be precise. That same day I got pulled out for the first time... Okay, I will tell you what I am. I'm last season's Premier League ball, you know like the yellow, red and blue one. If you don't know, it's fine but whoever was pumping me was very bad and I will tell you why... He pumped me way too much and it nearly made me burst into thin air! The next minute I was in a car, well I think that's what it's called anyway.

We got to the stadium finally, not to be rude! I saw the players come out and start training but the thing was, I was really sad, nervous and lonely waiting for the referee to come. That's when we started to play.

Oscar Dewey (10)

St Nicholas CE Primary School, Reading

My Trip To Thorpe Park

Dear Diary,

Today I went to Thorpe Park for the first time ever. It started when my parents told me that I was going. Me and my sister and my dad all went together. The ride was so long.

Soon after we got there, we saw all the tall rides over the very tall bushes and when we got to the park and checked in, we were ready to go on the rides. I wasn't scared at all but there was one ride that did scare me, the ride called Stealth.

After I had conquered my fear of Stealth we had some snacks. I refused to eat any food because I didn't want to get sick on any of the rides.

Later we went on some water rides and they were so wet. We stayed there for eight hours and it was the best day. I can't wait to go back in the future. Violet.

Violet Boyden (10)

St Nicholas CE Primary School, Reading

1 Vs 1

Dear Diary,

Today felt like a dream. I went to Milwaukee to play against Giannis Antetokumpo and his brother as I am the best in Europe. When I woke up I was super pumped as they live in Milwaukee. We had to wake up super early so that we could get there in time and started driving. If we had the money we would have taken a plane. It's not easy to drive to America and it took 19 hours but we soon got to Coral Reef and got food and finally we ended up in Milwaukee, Wisconsin. Even though I was nervous I was still excited.

We started and they were winning and then I scored ten points and won. I was so happy and everyone congratulated me and I gave out a signed basketball and shirt and we started the journey back home.

Lucas Jaworski (9)
St Nicholas CE Primary School, Reading

The Dream

Dear Diary,

I've never looked forward to something in my life and then I finally got to do my dream. In fact, I couldn't sleep on Thursday or Friday because I was so excited for Saturday.

Luckily it was only a five-minute journey and when we arrived I saw the most massive, prettiest house I had ever seen in my life. It was pearl white with incredible furniture. I was offered some food, it was delicious.

After that got dressed in my fairy costume and I had a puffy blue dress with glitter everywhere and I had my Shetland ready to be a unicorn.

Me and my aunt, who was dressed as a cowgirl with a horse, stood there for one and a half hours talking to people and letting them take our photo.

Sammy Jones (9)
St Nicholas CE Primary School, Reading

Definitely Not A Beetastic Day

Dear Diary,

Today was terrible, I don't know where to start...
Well, I will begin with the first thing that happened.
I was in the meadow and it was lovely, I was
pollinating flowers until some kid whacked me out
of the air. Wait till you hear what happened next...
The next thing was terrible! I mean, it was so
terrible as he hit me so hard that my wing was no
longer buzzy and I was supposed to be entered
into a bee competition for the most buzziest bee! I
still entered but only got 4th place! I would have
won if it wasn't for that kid! I would have got a lot
of honey as a prize. Since I only got 4th place, all I
got was a droplet of honey!
From your not-so-buzzy friend,
Bee.

Willow Gregory (10)
St Nicholas CE Primary School, Reading

The Whiteboard

Dear Diary,

Today was the most stressful day of my whole entire life. No day had ever been as painful as this! I was just sitting on my wall when someone took me from my comfort zone and then suddenly a herd of monsters grabbed me and started drawing one. Talk about rude! One of the monsters even licked me! Ewwww! Then my ally, the whiteboard rubber, cleaned me but a monster dropped me and then a chair squished me with its chair leg. I remained there until my nice master, the teacher, picked me up and put me back on my wall. For a few hours, I was comfortable, dreaming about being free until the next day when it all repeated again.

Caleb Chan (10)

St Nicholas CE Primary School, Reading

Thorpe Park

Dear Diary,

I went to Thorpe Park and the park was really big. There was so much there to do. I went with my grandma on the teacups and the teacups were fast. My grandma said, "Oh my goodness!" My family were with me to play the 4-D. It was so so fun! There was also a playground as well as many more fun things to do. Thorpe Park also has a beach. I liked the beach, it was cool. My mum made me a packed lunch and it was very yummy. Me and my family like to go there.

Giovanna Wan (10)

St Nicholas CE Primary School, Reading

The Bumble Girl

Dear Diary,

Today was the worst day ever. In fact, picture one of those movies where everything starts and you see a little glimmer of hope but then things turn out worse than before. That was my day!

First of all the day started in the worst possible way. How you ask? Well, I woke up with a pounding headache because we had this writing project in school where we had to write a report on a topic of our choice and unfortunately I picked the history of Priorville as my topic. I had worked late into the night on my laptop.

After my horrible morning, I saw my best friend Stephenie Smith at lunch then out of the shadows came Vickie Gold AKA a popular senior. She was captain of the Priorville Cheerleaders but what happened next wasn't expected... I started to get suspicious when Vickie ordered a milkshake as she was lactose intolerant.

All of a sudden she started sashaying towards me and then she poured the milkshake down my shirt. She then had the audacity to say, "You have never tasted so sweet!" As a result of this, everybody then started to call me Sweet Bumble. I went as

red as a tomato. I had never been so embarrassed. I am the definition of embarrassed and so that was my day!
Elliana Bumble.

Monjolaoluwa Olusola (10)
St Patrick's Catholic Primary School, Birmingham

A Morning In The Life Of A Cat

Dear Diary,

Today was a good day, lots of sleeping, food, cuddles, meowing and purrs. First of all I woke up in my favourite part of the house, my bed of course! After twenty minutes of stretching, I woke my owner Viktoria up.

"Meow," I said as I jumped on her bed.

"Hi, Bruno!" she said.

Do you know that without me, my owner would always be late for school? She seemed to be always sleeping! I do a great job of going to my owner's room and standing on two legs with the help of the bed, it is a daily routine for me.

I decided to then cuddle up to my owner as there was no point getting up too early and I was a very hard-working cat. You see, it was also a very painful and sad time for me when my owner has to go off to school. Couldn't she pet me all day instead? Why does she even have to go to school? After thinking about how hard-working I am, I decided to go to sleep but Bella, my wife, would be angry as we were supposed to have a meeting. I decided to have a rest anyway and this is my daily morning routine!

Viktoria Wojcik (10)

St Patrick's Catholic Primary School, Birmingham

Aliens Vs Humans

Dear Diary,

Aliens are always misunderstood. Humans look at aliens in the wrong way. They say we are big and blue or even small and red. We sometimes get told we have three big googly eyes sticking out of our bum! We don't! We look exactly like humans! We have two eyes, two ears, one nose and a human body. Now don't get me started on our way of connection. They say we talk like 'mee moo mah' or 'gabbah gab gab' - that one drives me crazy! Also so does the stupid, quirky robot beeps, why do some humans think we talk like robots? We don't! Maybe it's because their stupid minds don't work properly. We're smarter than AIs (despite the fact we were born in never-ending darkness). Anyway, I was sitting on Planet Dacloria when I realised humans don't even know where we live. They say we live on the moon or on Mars. We don't! We live on Planet Decoria. After all this given evidence, dear Diary, all I can say about these fellow humans is... humans are dumb!

Hannah Vipin (10)

St Patrick's Catholic Primary School, Birmingham

Awful Adventures

Dear Diary,

I have no idea how it all happened... I was in bed sleeping like any other person would be and the sky was dark and luminous but tonight was different and I still ended up falling asleep. Glimmering was the first thing I saw. I mean, I woke up with poor eyes. I screamed as I saw a metallic figure. Squinting my eyes I realised it was a robot. I thought they only existed in movies!

"Hello, Alice right?" the robot questioned.

"Stop talking! Why am I here? I have school!" I shrieked.

The robot grabbed my arm and dragged me towards a strange, glowing, floating thing. "Wait, is that a UFO?" I searched with my eyes around the place. "Is it supposed to be this cold? Why are there so many stars?"

The robot looked me up and down. "We're in space, relax and stop whining!" the robot said rudely.

My pupils widened. He was definitely joking, right? This had to be a dream or some kind of joke...

Stacey Bansah (10)
St Patrick's Catholic Primary School, Birmingham

Going On A Journey With Parronk

Dear Diary,

Today was not what I was expecting. So every month I go visit my family on Magical Island since I live so far from them. I decided to go today and guess what? My powers were gone! It just happens randomly. I knew if I didn't go today my family would worry so I called my friend Parronk and he gave me a lift. I was like awesome because he's so strong! He holds me like I am being captured by a seagull.

The journey took about two days to get there by flying so I strapped my suitcase onto his back and he didn't feel anything. Soon we were whizzing off in the sky. I was basically wet since we had to whizz through clouds and clouds had water. He could walk on clouds but without my power I couldn't. I was hungry so we sat on a cloud and I had to sit on his shoulders to eat peacefully. Then we continued our journey.

Soon I saw the unicorn statue and we had arrived. Me and Parronk stayed at my family's place for a week.

Georgina Sarker (10)

St Patrick's Catholic Primary School, Birmingham

The Lonely Kid

Dear Diary,

My name is Max Brown and I am ten years old. I live in the UK. Today I am going to tell you about my day at school. Every morning I am not really excited to go to school because I always get bullied by these two girls called Rejina and Lucy. They always bully me and call me a loser, loner and a nerd.

We were in class and studying maths and Regina and Lucy called me the teacher's pet for doing my homework and knowing the answers to every question. Finally I was sick of it so I told Mr Tom, our teacher, and he gave them a warning card. I then made my way to Mrs Vivian who is the head teacher and I said, "Sorry to disturb you, I just wanted to talk to you about something. Rejina and Lucy are bullying me and calling me names like loser, nerd and teacher's pet."

After that, the message got passed over to their parents and the head teacher suspended them. After they come back, they will never bully me again!

Avneet Kaur (9)

St Patrick's Catholic Primary School, Birmingham

The Lizard Man

Dear Diary,

It was just a normal day at Lizard Museum. I was just relaxing in my cage when suddenly a teenager came up to me (I'm pretty sure his name is Sam). He started tapping on the glass. I got angry and hissed at him. You should have seen his face. You will then not believe what happened... He knocked my cage on the floor and I got so annoyed that I bit him. But he started let's say 'acting weird' and then he rushed to the toilet. I followed him and while I was peeking through the toilet door, I saw him grow a tail and he started screaming. Then his tongue got so big and sticky and then he said, "What on earth is happening?" I could not resist and laughed but as I am an animal he did not hear me. He said, "I can now be a hero, whoopie! My name is going to be Sam the Super Lizard!" I thought he was a strange boy and what he was saying was not going to come true but anyway, that's it for today!

Felipe V Torres Martins (10)
St Patrick's Catholic Primary School, Birmingham

My Life As A Mop

Dear Diary,

Why is it always me that is doing a bad job of things? I mop the floor but my owner says I've done a horrible job... just mop the floor yourself! Imagine being bitten by your friend every day. That must be horrible! Guess what, I'm that one thing that's being bit! I don't know how I'm writing this, given I don't have any hands or feet but I am. Anyways, yes, I got bit by a friend. My only friend, as dog named Stella. She doesn't know how to speak, only bark. Anyway, neither do I so let's cut to the chase. Oh wait, sorry, I have not introduced myself, my name is Penelopey and I am eleven years old and I think you know my one friend already. My life is horrible. I get verbally abused and if you think that sounds fun, it's not. It's actually horrible. I'm almost at the end of the page now, so I will have to stop writing.

Until next time, Diary. Bye!

Maja Leks (10)

St Patrick's Catholic Primary School, Birmingham

Anna's Trip To the Philippines

Dear Diary,

Today is the day I am going to go to the Philippines to meet my family because they live there. I have been practising the language and just in case I forget a word I'm taking my Tagalog book. Now let's see, I have got my toiletries, clothes, shoes, skincare, underwear, sunglasses, sunscreen and my book. I think that's it, now I have to go and catch my flight at 03:00 and it's 2:30 now!

Dear Diary,

As soon as I got on the plane it was amazing. I'm on the plane now. The seats are so nice and there is a lot of room. They have the best food as well and there is a TV on the back of the seat in front. Economy class is still luxurious!

Dear Diary,

I've arrived. I was surprised to see all of my family waiting for me at the airport. I hugged all of them. I hope this holiday will be the best holiday ever!

Breana Andrada (10)

St Patrick's Catholic Primary School, Birmingham

158

A Gym Day

Dear Diary,

Today was the best day ever. I went to gymnastics and I am going to tell you what I did. First I did my warm-up by doing some running and then doing some jumping and hopping down the track. I then did a lot of conditioning and when I started on the competition track I noticed it was the hardest track in the gym!

On the competition track, I worked on my full twist. Next we went upstairs on the soft track and I worked on my full twist again. Because me and my friends worked so hard we got to play a game called 'stick the landing'. There were two teams. Team one: Taylor, Amelia, Melissa and me. Team two: Zach, Jessica, Lily, Lottie and Lucy. As we had fewer people we got the head start. We then did conditioning because it was Wednesday. Next we stretched and then we packed up and went home.

Zenayah Bennett-McLean (10)

St Patrick's Catholic Primary School, Birmingham

Mine And Binny's Problems

Dear Diary,

I was at school, minding my own business, when Binny came up to me and bullied me as usual. I didn't tell the teacher because if I told the teacher everyone would think I was a stitch.

At lunchtime, I was lining up for lunch when Binny pushed me. I was like, "What the hell are you doing, man?" Well, I didn't say that out loud.

I sat alone at the table and then Binny showed up at my table and I said in my mind, "What do you want now?"

He said to me, "Give me your lunch?"

I shouted, "No!" Then he spilt all the food on my head. I had now had enough so I went to the principal's office and explained what happened and he got expelled! I was so happy but sad at the same time. However, I am relieved and can be popular now.

Barakat Adeoti (10)

St Patrick's Catholic Primary School, Birmingham

The World Depends On You!

Dear Diary,

The scariest thing ever just happened to me. Me, yes me, Captain Cool. Shocking right? So it went like this... I was training in my secret base for my battle against my arch-enemy Dr Boring but then I tried to use my happy ray and I couldn't. I tried and tried but nothing happened. I was terrified so I called my best friend and he said he could fix it but I would go through extreme pain. At this point, I didn't care about the pain. Dr Boring would destroy the world if I didn't stop him so I stepped into the machine and when it was turned on, it burnt like crazy. I didn't care.

The battle started and I rushed to him. I shot him an endless amount of times until he was gone and I had saved the world.

M'Kai Baker (10)

St Patrick's Catholic Primary School, Birmingham

The Super Triplets

Dear Diary,

Me, Even and Yugi were playing when a bully came and he punched us all.

When school ended we went home and then our mum told us something. She said, "Boys, you have powers!" We were surprised.

Two days later we had found our powers. I had lighting, shape-shifting and earth powers, Even had flying, strength and fire powers and Yugi had fire, ice and telekinesis. We were now super triplets and we rushed off to defeat the villains and our greatest enemy was Louis who flew away when he saw us but was still out there!

Thirty years later the villains came back and some children told us their parents had died. We wanted revenge so we battled but we lost. Then reinforcements came and we won.

Giovanni Obumnemenare (9)
St Patrick's Catholic Primary School, Birmingham

My Morning

Dear Diary,

Today I woke up at 8:30am then I started walking slowly to the kitchen and I made myself cereal. I went to the bathroom, brushed my teeth and I got changed into clothes. I then grabbed my brush and when I finished brushing my hair it was 7:30am so I drew and watched TV until 8:10am.

It was now time I had to go to school so I hopped into the car and arrived at 8:30. I had to wait for the gate to open and then I walked down the long stairs and hung up my coat inside the classroom. It was 9:45 and time went so quickly.

When I was done with maths, the teacher asked a last hard question and it was so hard and I struggled.

Finally it was break and I had a lot of fun playing with my friends.

Nikola Kondraciuk (10)

St Patrick's Catholic Primary School, Birmingham

The Wonderful Adventures Of Beep Boop

Dear Diary,

My name's Beep Boop and today was the weirdest day ever. When I woke up I was in a different world and it was really noisy. There were so many people but not normal people, they all had antennae on their heads and the cars weren't on the ground, they were hovering!

I ran and ran so fast I couldn't see my legs. Every time I stopped I just slid in another direction. Then I finally stopped and I was standing on something green. Something soft. Something soothing.

I started running again and I was back to where I was. I saw my mum and dad and they were by the clock called Big Ben. "Mum, Dad, wait up!" I said but they left me.

There was one car left so I got in it...

Judah Haylett (10)
St Patrick's Catholic Primary School, Birmingham

Enough Is Enough

Dear Diary,

As a football, people always like to kick me. People don't know that I have emotions! The crazy thing is that they can't stop touching me even for a day. I always try to escape but they still find a way to get me. Every time I try not to get taken to a training or football match. They still take me though, with another twenty balls. I feel like a slave. Find someone else! Finally I do get a break. What is so great about football anyway? Can you not live without it, people? Stop kicking me, I always get blasted at metal posts! It's painful! What if someone did that to you? I would guess you would cry like a little girl!

Nicolas Gaweda (10)

St Patrick's Catholic Primary School, Birmingham

My Life As A Horse

Dear Diary,

I'm a horse and it's so tiring. I'm Thunder by the way. I hate birds, they creep me out. The kids that ride me love me and I kinda love them back. I jump super high and I scare the birds away when I jump. I don't get how kids fall off me. I don't do anything and I sometimes feel sorry for them. I love the fields but there are so many birds! The nine-year-olds though kick me so hard! Whips are fine so long as they don't tap me a lot with them. Okay, shall I talk about the birds? Why do they shout so loud? It really hurts my ears. Anyway, my life is wonderful!

Sophie Narojczyk (10)

St Patrick's Catholic Primary School, Birmingham

The Ball

Dear Diary,

Today was strange! Me and my friend Spongy were enjoying our McDonald's when suddenly a red ball came running towards us, it needed our help. It told us its name and then we introduced ourselves and we went through this strange machine.

When we came out, everything looked strange... We had gone back in time! Then we saw a red ball with a white circle and it was attacking people. I knew that it was wrong. Then it attacked us but we were too strong. Then balls from different countries came to help and after a long fight, we defeated the bad ball.

Given Kisula (10)

St Patrick's Catholic Primary School, Birmingham

Young Writers Information

We hope you have enjoyed reading this book – and that you will continue to in the coming years.

If you're the parent or family member of an enthusiastic poet or story writer, do visit our website **www.youngwriters.co.uk/subscribe** and sign up to receive news, competitions, writing challenges and tips, activities and much, much more! There's lots to keep budding writers motivated!

If you would like to order further copies of this book, or any of our other titles, then please give us a call or order via your online account.

Young Writers
Remus House
Coltsfoot Drive
Peterborough
PE2 9BF
(01733) 890066
info@youngwriters.co.uk

Join in the conversation!
Tips, news, giveaways and much more!

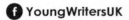 YoungWritersUK   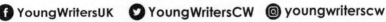YoungWritersCW   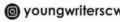 youngwriterscw

Scan me to watch The Incredible Diary Of video!